pedestrian

planning and design

Revised Edition

John J. Fruin, Ph.D.

ELEVATOR WORLD, INC.
Educational Services Division
P.O. Box 6507
354 Morgan Avenue
Mobile, Alabama 36606

First Printing: 1971
Editor: Dr. Edmund J. Cantilli
Design and Graphics: Mr. Bartolo Basile

Second Printing: 1987
Revision Editor: George R. Strakosch

PEDESTRIAN PLANNING AND DESIGN

Library of Congress Catalog Number 70-159312

This revised edition of the original "Pedestrian Planning and Design" first published by the Metropolitan Association of Urban Designers and Environmental Planners, Inc. in 1971, has been made possible by the efforts of Dr. Fruin and Elevator World Inc., Educational Services Division.

As foremost supporters of proper and safe pedestrian transportation and recognizing the need for proper and safe access to such transportation as well as the areas in and around buildings, Elevator World is pleased to make this book available to planners, architects, building owners and managers, vertical and horizontal transportation specialists and all who are concerned with improving our urban environment.

George Strakosch, Revisions Editor

PEDESTRIAN PLANNING AND DESIGN (Revised Edition) is published to foster and improve communication between the various factors responsible for planning and designing facilities used by the public. The author and publisher suggest that the material be used as stimulation to thinking and not as directives. They publish this material without accepting responsibility for its absolute accuracy, but with hope that the vast majority of it will have validity for the field. The ideas expressed therein should be tempered by recognized engineering practices, guidelines, codes and standards.

PEDESTRIAN PLANNING AND DESIGN (Revised Edition) is available from Elevator World, Inc., Educational Services Division, P.O. Box 6507, Loop Branch, Mobile, AL 36606.

Preface

The title "Pedestrian Planning and Design" may be considered by some to be a misnomer, since only the Good Lord can plan or design a pedestrian. The intent of the book, however, is to help fill the broad gap that exists in the planning and design of building and street spaces for comfortable and convenient human use. Much of this book is based on the author's dissertation, "Designing for Pedestrians", but this title was not used because it did not fully convey the objective and scope intended.

The beginning of the book establishes the importance of walking in urban design, and the problems of pedestrians in today's cities. There is a brief insight into some of the human physiological and psychological factors that affect the planning and design of pedestrian spaces. The traffic and space characteristics of pedestrians are developed in sufficient detail for an understanding of pedestrian traffic relationships. Supplementary written and pictorial descriptions of pedestrian traffic interactions at various human space occupancies provide a useful supplement for evaluating the environmental design quality of pedestrian building and street spaces.

The objectives of pedestrian planning programs, study procedures and methods of plan implementation are illustrated, and the design discussion is supplemented by illustrative examples. The book closes with a short review of some of the programs that are in progress for the improvement of the pedestrian environment.

John J. Fruin, Ph.D.

Contents

Chapter Five   Pedestrian Movers—"Pedmovers"

Chapter Six   Elements of Pedestrian Planning

Chapter Seven   Elements of Pedestrian Design

Chapter Eight   New Developments in Planned Pedestrian Environments

*"What a piece of work is man! How
noble in reason! how infinite in faculty;
in form, in moving, how express and
admirable! in action how like an angel!
in apprehension, how like a God! the beauty
of the world! the paragon of animals!"*
Hamlet, Act Two, Scene Two

Chapter One
PEDESTRIAN MAN

Walking is one of man's most magnificent abilities, a vital factor in his long journey up the evolutionary ladder and his progress towards civilization. Walking abilities shaped the first rudimentary human settlements and early cities. Because these cities were structured upon the convenience and comfort of the pedestrian, many of them were characterized by their human qualities of design. But the advent of machine transportation has caused a drastic restructuring of urban form, interposing the scale of the vehicle into urban design. The conflict of man and auto has created an unbalanced competition for urban space. The auto has pervaded all phases of urban structure, causing a dilution of the human environment. The auto kills and maims the pedestrian, it causes noise, dust and fumes, and is detrimental in its socio-economic impacts. It threatens the very quality and viability of urban life.

The Long Walk

About a million years ago, the antecedents of pedestrian man took the first steps on a journey to the stars. Fossil evidence suggests it was at about this time that the leg- and foot-bone development of the early hominid began to make upright walking possible. One can visualize this primitive human lifting his gaze to the heavens, and reaching up to grasp the moon as if picking fruit from a tree. It must have given him a new exhilaration to pull himself erect to his full height, but it must have also filled him with a burning curiosity about the inaccessibility of the moon and stars.

Darwin postulated that man's dominance of his environment began only after he gained the ability to walk erect, freeing his hands for the use of weapons and tools. Upright walking was a specialized human adaptation which was gradually evolved into the most efficient means of animal locomotion. It enabled man to cover long distances economically, opening up an entirely new spectrum of experience that became vital to his survival and development. Efficient locomotion allowed him to flee from danger or to leave limited and hostile environments. It made him a proficient hunter and food gatherer. The ever-widening ranges of the hunt moved him into encounters with the new and unexpected, forcing him to develop new skills and attitudes. The ever-increas-

1

ing prospects of new horizons contributed to insatiable human desires for exploration, discovery and knowledge.

About thirty-five thousand years ago, early man had completed his monumental evolutionary struggles and emerged as our more familiar species, pedestrian man. His range had extended from his first dependence on a tropical woodland savanna for protection and survival, to habitation of the mountain, prairie, desert and tundra. Still pondering the mysteries of the heavens, he turned his attention to the mastery and shaping of his environment. His walking ability had brought him to this point, and he was conscious of its importance to his continuing progress.

The Pedestrian and the City of the Past

Man's locomotive capabilities shaped the first primitive encampments and rudimentary cities. Walking distances determined their location, shape and size. The camp keepers required a protected enclave that could be reached quickly on foot at the first threat of danger. The food gatherers had to be within walking distance of edible wild plants, potable water and reliable hunting grounds. The bountifulness of the countryside would determine the number of inhabitants that could be supported. The hours of daylight limited the effective range of these primitive developments to about a ten- to fifteen-mile walk in any direction. The most efficient walkers, the hunters, were the leaders of these early communities. Because the hunter was aware of the use of natural features of topography for defensive advantage, he determined the location and form of the settlement. The success or failure of the hunt was a central theme of early religious cults, and the proficient hunter grew to be one to be respected and served. Because of their aggressiveness, their skills in the use of weapons and tactics, their strength and sharpened senses, the hunters became the first ruling class, dominating much of the early history of `man.

About five thousand years ago, the first truly organized cities were founded around religion-oriented monarchies supported by a large subservient population. The advent of organized agriculture and domestication of animals allowed an expansion of city size because it provided larger and more reliable sources of food. Usually, the inner city was walled, and the temple, storehouse and palace were situated behind the wall. The general populace camped outside. The hunter became the pedestrian soldier, protecting the ruler, administering and maintaining his justice and extending his influence.

In time, the institutional city gave way to a broader, more diversified type of development centered on collective defense. The walls of the city were extended, and a much larger population was housed within the perimeter. Careful attention was given to selecting locations that could be defended easily. Hilltops, peninsulas and islands became prime sites. Where natural topography was lacking, artificial defensive features were constructed. In some cases, the outer defensive wall became a physical restraint to city development, forcing denser clusters of dwellings and the first examples of multi-story buildings.

The great cities of history were built both to serve pedestrian man and to inspire him with social and religious cohesiveness. The placement and arrangement of the buildings and monuments of the Acropolis is said to have been based on human lines of sight and visual capabilities. When the Greeks entered the Acropolis, they wanted to view it as a unified whole, but with each building and statue individually discernible and not interfering with the other. Building shape, location and natural topography were used to attain this objective. The Acropolis is an example of the design of a space for human scale, without introducing the discontinuity of conflicting visual or physical elements.

The Parthenon of the ancient Acropolis (the "upper city"), overlooking modern Athens.

The ancient Romans and Hebrews recognized the disruption to scale caused by vehicular intrusion. Julius Caesar decreed that heavy wagons were forbidden within the central city after dusk. The Forum of Pompeii was an extensive pedestrian precinct comprised of seven culs-de-sac. Large slab-like stone barriers were placed at all entrance points to prevent intrusion by vehicles. The Talmud, the Hebraic book of laws, decreed that special areas should be set aside along main thoroughfares for pedestrians to unload their burdens and rest. These areas were to be clearly marked and separated from vehicular intrusion by a perimeter of metal spikes or stone bollards.

The need for human communication and interaction was recognized by medieval city planners by providing a central pedestrian plaza. It was designed as an open space to serve and visually complement the Cathedral and other important buildings located around its perimeter. The plaza was the market place, a place for public pronouncements, religious and festive occasions, and recreation. The size of the plaza was a function of the number of people who might come together for these purposes.

The human comfort and convenience of pedestrians was also not overlooked by medieval planners. Pedestrians were protected from the elements by gallerias, canopies, colonnades and porticos. The old city of Bologna has a twenty-mile network of sidewalks covered by porticos which provides a cool, dry, pedestrian way in the summer and one that is free from snow in winter. This latter aspect is significant in a mountain town that has its quota of snowstorms. Bologna's system of covered sidewalks has been admired by many famous writers and philosophers for its pleasurable strolling and the native sociability that it encourages. The covered, elevated sidewalk, a feature of some recent pedestrian proposals, also makes an occasional appearance in medieval architecture.

The great Leonardo da Vinci, master of all arts and sciences, recognized the value of grade-separated systems for pedestrian and vehicular traffic. He planned a city with a double network of streets, one elevated for pedestrians, the other at ground level to serve vehicles. Da Vinci, the engineer, recognized that the most efficient traffic system for both pedestrians and vehicles required separate, continuous networks for each. Da Vinci, the artist, recognized that the requirements of visual aesthetics could best be satisfied by a distinctive human perspective set above the city's milieu.

The medieval plaza was a place for human communication and interaction—Piazza San Marco, Venice.

The portico covered sidewalks of Bologna, Italy, protect pedestrians from the elements.

There also appears to have been at least some recognition by medieval planners that building floor area should be a function of street width. Medieval cities limited building heights to two times the width of the street. Da Vinci was of the opinion that a ratio of one to one was more desirable. This contrasts with some modern cities where pavement and sidewalk widths have remained constant for a century or more, while building heights have been extended by hundreds of feet. In many of these instances, sidewalk space has actually been reduced during this time to facilitate the movement of vehicles. The artisans of the past were not above adorning the sidewalks and streets with textured pavements and mosaics for both practical and aesthetic purposes. The cobblestone streets of old Milan were paved in such a way that carriage wheels were guided away from the walkway, thus preventing vehicles from swerving and hitting pedestrians. There is little evidence of this concern for the pedestrian in today's cities.

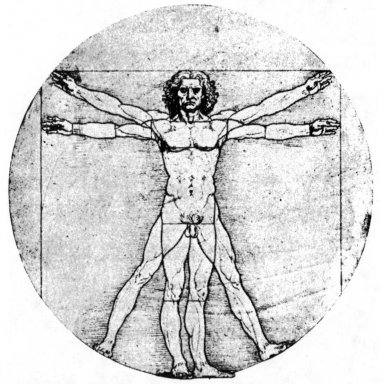

Leonardo Da Vinci's Man—the master's studies of human anatomy were reflected in his works of art and architecture.

The Pedestrian and the City of Today

Transportation, whether by walking or other means, has always been a significant determinant of the structure of the city. Because the internal transportation of the cities of the past was based on the convenience of walking, these cities were characterized by more attention to the human qualities of design. The advent of machine transportation has changed this perspective, forcing man into an unbalanced competition for urban space. The railroad made the first great incursions into the city, bringing tracks, noise, smoke and cinders. In some places the railroads virtually obliterated large sections of the city, paving them with ribbons of steel. But the railroad is confined to its tracks, which can be hidden underground if necessary. The ubiquity of the auto has introduced much broader demands for space, pervading every part of the urban structure, confronting man at every turn, causing a vast dichotomy in the goals of city planning and design.

Despite its advantages of personal mobility, the auto is responsible for a great many negative changes in our society. It is a force that has imposed itself on every aspect of urban life, destroying many of the elements that made cities cohesive units dedicated to the social and cultural advancement of their inhabitants. The auto's fumes contaminate the air, and its noise and vibration disturb sleep, conversation or contemplation. It kills and maims pedestrian man, forcing him to remain constantly alert and vigilant lest their paths cross. It imposes its *scale* upon urban design, requiring the allocation of vast amounts of space for its movement and storage. It isolates pedestrian man in a limited, ever-narrowing sidewalk environment, reducing opportunities for human social interaction and visual enjoyment. It has produced a visual clutter of traffic signals and signs. It is a source of frustration and humiliation to the pedestrian, who is not only forced to wait in the rain and snow while the autoist in his climatized capsule environment enjoys traffic priority, but who may even be honked at or splashed if he does not react quickly enough.

The street and building spaces of the Urban Core or Central Business District magnify these problems because of their intensive concentration of pedestrians. The Central Business District (CBD) is usually comprised of variable land uses: office buildings, government centers, shopping and entertainment centers, restaurants, historical sites, and, in some cases, high-rise residential developments. The CBD is the focal point of the regional transportation network, and the center of confluence of transit and highways. Because of its infinite diversity, walking is the only means of transportation that can satisfy the many short, dispersed trip linkages required within the Central Business District. Downtown origin and destination surveys show that, in most cities, about ninety per cent of all internal trips within the CBD are walking trips.

The traditional urban core is usually superimposed on an archaic street system surviving from the land use and functional scale of the past. The street system of the downtown financial district of Manhattan, for example, is a survivor from colonial times, when the tallest structure was of two or three stories. Now these same streets serve buildings that rise 50 to 100 stories in the air, representing millions of square feet of office space. Thousands of workers and visitors enter and leave these buildings each day, exceeding the capacity of the sidewalk and spilling over into the roadway. In a situation like this, maximum use of sidewalk area and flow capacity is a necessity.

The advent of machine transportation has forced man into an unbalanced competition for urban space.

In many high-density Central Business Districts, the sidewalk width has actually been reduced to facilitate vehicular traffic movement. This results in a reduction of pedestrian traffic capacity, but does not always produce a commensurate increase in vehicular capacity. The wider streets increase the probabilities of pedestrian-vehicle crosswalk conflicts, which limit the vehicular capacity of the intersection. The potential pedestrian capacity of the CBD sidewalks is reduced further by the intrusion of various sidewalk impedimenta. Refuse cans, fire hydrants, fire alarm boxes, parking meters, traffic signals and poles, newsstands, telephone booths, kiosks, mail boxes, planters, sewer and ventilation gratings and similar devices detract from sidewalk capacity. In addition, building-service operations, such as the unloading or loading of trucks inconvenience, and sometimes endanger, the pedestrian. In many instances, no control has been exercised over the location of fixed sidewalk paraphernalia, and they often appear in clusters at corner intersections, the most critical points in the pedestrian circulation network. Space is

A conglomeration of sidewalk paraphernalia blocking a pedestrian crosswalk.

needed at intersection corners for accumulations of pedestrians waiting for traffic signals and for the weaving of intersecting sidewalk flows. Because of its concentrations of traffic, the corner is the ideal location for newsstands, telephone booths and mail boxes. It is also the most common location for transit-bus stops and rapid transit entrances. The pedestrian is further harassed at the corner by vehicles stopped in the crosswalk, or turning into crossing pedestrians. When a rapid transit entrance is situated within a narrow sidewalk near an intersection, it is an outstanding example of compounded insensitivity to the pedestrian. Because the sidewalk itself is narrow, excessively narrow subway stairs are provided, causing pedestrian queues both in the transit station below and on the surface above at the point where pedestrian space is already critically deficient. All these factors add up to inconvenience and delay for the pedestrian. But despite the fact that the total amount of pedestrian delay time may far exceed driver delay time within the CBD, traffic signalization is invariably designed to facilitate vehicular flow.

A narrow subway stair placed within a narrow city sidewalk.

The rectangular grid pattern of the typical CBD provides a good directional image and space delineation, but it is not conducive to the characteristically short pedestrian trips that occur there. In some instances, the grid pattern of Manhattan's streets require a time-and energy-consuming 1000 foot walk for a straight-line trip distance of only 200 feet. Larger mid-block buildings with frontages on adjacent streets are often used as through-routes, so that the pedestrian can shorten trip distances. This practice is more common in inclement weather. Depending on city location, one day in four may be too windy, cold or wet for the pedestrian's comfort. Protection of the pedestrian from the elements is an almost forgotten amenity in most cities.

Intense vehicular utilization of city streets is causing significant socio-economic impacts on urban life which are only now beginning to be recognized. A sociological study of nearby residential streets in the same neighborhood in San Francisco, subjected to light and heavy traffic, gives a partial insight into this problem. The streets were physically alike in almost all respects except that the sidewalk on the heavy-traffic street had been narrowed to facilitate vehicular movement. In addition, sound-meter samples on the heavy-traffic street showed that sound levels were above 65 decibels at the sidewalk 45 per cent of the time, as contrasted to 5 per cent for the light-traffic street. Despite the physical similarities of the streets, drastic differences in social attitudes and neighborhood identity were noted between the two streets.

The light-traffic street was predominantly a family street, with individually owned homes and an average length of residence of 16 years. The heavy-traffic street was comprised of nearly all renters, with few children and an average length of residence of 8 years. Social interaction and neighborhood identity and interest differed widely on the two streets. Residents on the light-traffic street were found to have three times as many local friends as those on the heavy-traffic street. Residents on the light-traffic street were found to have a greater sense of neighborhood and territorial identity, striving more to maintain and improve their homes. The heavy-traffic street residents stressed their concern for safety, and the continual invasions of privacy caused by the passing autos. They also indicated greater concern over noise, dust, fumes and vibration. Elderly residents of this street exhibited more emotional stress than those of the light-traffic street.

Pedestrian Safety

In 1969, 56,400 people were killed by motor vehicle accidents in the United States. Of this total, 9,800, or 17.4 per cent, were pedestrians. In addition, 150,000 pedestrians were injured by motor vehicles. This loss of human life and the suffering caused by these accidents is a serious national problem. The economic cost in salary loss and medical expenses exceeds one-half billion dollars annually.

The majority of adult pedestrian fatality victims are persons who have not been licensed to drive. The pedestrian who has never driven faces special hazards, because he is unfamiliar with the limitations of the vehicle or driver. He is not aware of the driver's limited vision, particularly at night, nor is he capable of estimating a car's minimum stopping distance at various speeds. The child pedestrian is an especially vulnerable accident victim because of gaps in language, perception, and visual and auditory comprehension. Many aspects of human perception, such as peripheral vision, depth perception, judgement of speed and direction, and sound recognition, are attained through experience, which the child pedestrian has not yet acquired. This lack of experience causes not only perceptual difficulties, but uncertain reactions under the stress of frightening or unusual confrontations with moving traffic. In addition, children do not comprehend road signs, or if they do, they do not fully understand their responsibilities to obey these signs.

The stratification of accident statistics by age also shows a disproportionate involvement risk for the young, and a higher severity risk for the elderly. In the United States, more than one-half of the pedestrians injured came from the one-third of the population that is under 14 years of age. One-quarter of the fatalities occurred in the less than ten per cent of the population over age 65. Surprisingly, male pedestrians comprise more than two-thirds of all pedestrian accident victims, including fatalities.

Weather and darkness significantly affect pedestrian accident rates. Pedestrian casualties have been found to triple with darkness, with a similar three-fold increase on rainy versus clear days. The combination of rainfall and darkness increases the pedestrian accident risk factor by more than nine. It is not commonly known, but alcohol is a contributing factor in about one-quarter of all pedestrian deaths. Alcohol dulls the pedestrian's sense of judgement, and gives him a false feeling of confidence that is conducive to greater risk-taking.

12

The confusion created by the lack of a uniform national system of traffic laws and traffic control devices, recognized by motorist and pedestrian alike, is causing unnecessary pedestrian casualties.

Pedestrian fatalities are primarily an urban problem, with two-thirds of all deaths occurring in urban areas. However, accident studies of eleven major cities show that despite the heavy concentrations of pedestrians in central business districts, they were found to account for only about 14 per cent of all city pedestrian casualities. This is due to lower allowable speeds in the central business district and greater driver awareness of heavier pedestrian traffic. About two-thirds of all pedestrian accidents in the central business district occur at intersections, suggesting that special attention must be given to these points. Although it is generally believed that turning vehicles represent the greatest hazard to the pedestrians at intersections, about two-thirds of intersection accidents involve cars that are moving straight ahead. Of this total, more than half occur after the vehicle has left the near crosswalk. Left-turning vehicles are involved in about twice as many accidents as right-turning vehicles. Crossing between intersections has a higher severity risk, accounting for more than one-third of all urban pedestrian deaths.

Reduction of the pedestrian accident toll is a national problem which is being treated at the local level with varying degrees of concern. Although some standardization of pedestrian signs and signals has been recommended in the Manual of Uniform Traffic Control Devices, the manual itself has two standards for pedestrian signals, one for neon tube signs with a green WALK and a red DON'T WALK indication, and the other for incandescent signals with white WALK and orange DON'T WALK indication. A survey, comprised of questionnaire returns from more than 1600 cities, illustrated the confusion arising from the lack of a uniform method of pedestrian signalization. Based on survey returns, 38 per cent of the cities used the orange DON'T WALK indication, 56 per cent used red, and the remaining 6 per cent used white or other colors. The white WALK standard was used by 49 per cent of the cities, green 44 per cent, with the remaining 7 per cent using other colors. More than one-third of the respondents to the survey were not using the flashing DON'T WALK indication for the end of the walk cycle. Similar confusion exists in pedestrian signing and traffic laws. Some states have strong pedestrian right-of-way laws, while others do not. Motorists and pedestrians accustomed to signs, signals, and rules in one part of the country may be confronted by significant differences in another. The lack of a uniform national approach to pedestrian safety causes confusion for both motorist and pedestrian, and undoubtedly results in unnecessary pedestrian casualties. Pedestrian safety is a problem that crosses all state lines. This requires the establishment of a national system of traffic laws, traffic signalization and signs, implemented uniformly throughout the country, with Federal assistance if necessary.

The Handicapped Pedestrian

An estimated 12 million persons in the United States have serious physical disabilities which limit their mobility and the activities and work that they may do. The seriously handicapped include 250,000 in wheel chairs, 2 million orthopedically impaired children and 5 million cardiac cases. Each year, 100,000 children are born with birth defects that will force them to use crutches, braces or wheel chairs for the rest of their lives. In addition to these serious disabilities, many millions have minor sight deficiencies or other physical impairments which limit their locomotive capabilities. Added to the ranks of permanently handicapped pedestrians are the aged, whose motor capabilities have slowed down, persons temporarily disabled due to accidents and persons encumbered with baby carriages, heavy baggage or packages. The ranks of the physically handicapped have been expanding much faster than the general population growth because:

- medical advances have decreased the number of accidental deaths, thus increasing the number of disabled;

- longer average life spans have increased the number of aged and infirm; and

- more leisure time, greater personal mobility, and expanded opportunities for recreation have increased accident exposure for all persons.

Because of thoughtless architectural barriers, many of these persons have been denied opportunities for education, employment and recreation. Although they comprise a large segment of the public, they have been denied access to many "public" buildings and transit systems. This has relegated many of the aged and handicapped to the status of disenfranchised citizens, denied free access to the courts, polling places or public educational and cultural institutions. There are instances where handicapped citizens have been unable to attend court to defend their own interests. At best, they are often required to use freight elevator facilities, commonly used for refuse removal.

High curbs and sewer gratings cause difficulties for all pedestrians, but particularly the handicapped.

Long flights of stairs present a formidable obstacle to the handicapped pedestrian.

The common barriers to the aged and handicapped include: steps or curbs that are too high; long flights of stairs; inaccessible elevators; steep and narrow walks; gratings in walkways; doors that are too narrow, revolve, or are hard to open; too-narrow aisles in theatres, stadiums and other public gathering places; and lack of accommodations for wheelchairs. In addition, little if any consideration has been given to improving the mobility and safety of the blind and partially sighted, by supplementary auditory or tactile means. Needless to say, every effort should be made to improve the personal mobility and quality of life for these persons subjected to the daily hardships connected with their disabilities. Furthermore, improvements made for the aged and the handicapped are improvements which ease the mobility of all.

The international symbol of access, to be displayed on buildings without architectural barriers to the handicapped.

Chapter Two

HUMAN CHARACTERISTICS RELATED TO PEDESTRIAN DESIGN

The qualitative design of a pedestrian environment requires a basic understanding of related human characteristics and capabilities. The physical dimensions of the body determine working widths of doorways and passageways, and affect the practical capacity of moving stairs and walkways. Psychological preferences of avoiding bodily contact with others is a determinant of inter-person spacing in queues and other crowded pedestrian environments. Normal human locomotion involves many complex characteristics of balance, timing and even human sight, which are often taken for granted by all but the handicapped. Natural, free-speed locomotion requires spacial components for pacing and for human sensing and reaction. Human locomotion exhibits different characteristics on level surfaces and on stairs, with the latter requiring much more attention to design because of safety and energy expenditure. The perception of urban space is related to its coherence of expression. Confused spacial design lowers human receptivity to aesthetics and other secondary visual inputs.

Human Body Dimensions — The Body Ellipse

Body depth and shoulder breadth are the primary human measurements used by designers of pedestrian spaces and facilities. Shoulder breadth is a factor affecting the practical capacity of doorways, passageways, stairways and mechanical devices such as escalators and moving walks. Many of these facilities are ostensibly designed to allow two or more persons to pass through abreast, but actually have insufficient portal width for this purpose, limiting their convenience and capacity. For example, a moving-walk manufacturer offers a "double width" unit with a tread width of only 36 inches. This is insufficient to accommodate the normal space requirements of two persons standing abreast or walking parallel to each other. Observations of the use of this type of moving walk reveals that a single pedestrian with baggage or parcels can restrict both the boarding of other pedestrians and their potential locomotion on the walk after boarding.

A compilation of body dimensions from a large number of human-factors studies shows a shoulder breadth of 20.7 inches for the 99th percentile (99 per cent are less than this) of civilian men, with a recommended addition of 1½ inches for heavy clothing. A similar study of fully clothed male laborers gave a body depth dimension of 13.0 inches, and a shoulder breadth of 22.8 inches, for the 95th percentile. The larger male body dimensions have been quoted because, generally, a larger body ellipse has been used in most design applications.

BODY ELLIPSE

The plan view of the average adult male human body occupies an area of about 1½ square feet. An 18 by 24 inch body ellipse, equivalent to an area of 2.3 square feet, has been used to determine the practical standing capacity of New York City subway cars. A U.S. Army human factors design manual also recommends the use of these dimensions. The larger design ellipse allows for the fact that many pedestrians are carrying personal articles, natural psychological preferences to avoid bodily contact with others, and body sway. Body sway may be observed during both human locomotion and while standing. Although standing is generally considered a static activity, body sway and foot-shifting are required to aid in the return of blood to the brain and the resting of leg muscles.

The elliptical body template, drawn to scale, provides a simple and convenient method of visualizing many situations involving confined pedestrians. A 45-degree elliptical template, with various size ellipses, will give the designer sufficient range for a number of different scale applications. The body template technique is used to develop standards for queuing in Chapter Three.

The Perception of Personal Space — The Body Buffer Zone

Humans value personal space. As they acquire status and wealth they select larger offices, automobiles and homes. The pedestrian has his own personal space preferences which are related to his sense of "territory" and body image. If freedom of choice exists, pedestrians will adopt personal spacing which avoids contact with others, except in special circumstances such as a crowded elevator, where this unwritten law may be temporarily suspended.

20

Pedestrian conduct on sidewalks and other walkways is governed by personal body buffer zone concepts and hierarchical priorities of age, status, sex and handicaps. The average pedestrian has been found to yield the right of way to more aggressive or formidable-looking pedestrians, couples or other identifiable groups, and the aged and handicapped. In dense traffic streams this requires a deferential step-and-slide movement, by which the yielding pedestrian turns sideways to reduce his bodily projection in the walkway space. In more crowded conditions, both approaching pedestrians may yield and turn to avoid contact with each other. All these territorial rules of conduct go on quite unnoticed by most pedestrians, but personal space preferences are of interest to the designer because inter-person spacing of pedestrians affects the practical and comfortable environmental capacity of such facilities as theatre lobbies, elevators and escalators.

Hall, an anthropologist, has observed that there are different cultural attitudes towards personal space throughout the world. Many eastern and mideastern societies accept much closer spacing and a greater degree of personal contact than is normally tolerated by Americans. The larger inter-person spacing preferred by Americans is often interpreted as aloofness in these countries, producing an unintentioned communication gap. Hall's studies led him to the classification of spacial distances based on human sensory characteristics. (appendix reference) He established four general categories; public distance, social distance, personal distance, and intimate distance, with close and far phases in each category. These classifications are based on sensory shifts due to the changing characteristics of sight, smell, thermal receptivity, hearing and capabilities of touch at varying distances.

At public distances beyond twenty-five feet, there is limited sensory involvement, since very little of the personal detail of others can be detected. Oral communication is characterized by loudness and more exaggerated and stylized enunciation. Most actors know that at this distance the non-verbal elements of communication must be emphasized, including body stance, gestures and movement. At public distances of from twelve to twenty-five feet, the voice remains stylized, but volume is decreased and there is less emphasis on gesture and stance. Facial expressions, such as a frown or a smile, may be detected, but not facial details such as eye color, skin texture and the condition of the teeth. This is the probable range of the human "flight" zone, wherein an alert subject can take evasive or defensive action if threatened.

At twelve feet, social distance, or the circle of personal involvement and potential vulnerability, begins. In the historical context, it might be compared to the circle within which two combatants with fencing foils would parry and thrust (*"en garde!"*). Most formal business and conversation is conducted at the social distance of seven to twelve feet. By extending the body and stretching the arms, objects may be passed from one person to another. The finest details of the face are not yet discernible, but the condition of the clothes and other aspects of personal grooming may be detected. Heat or odor from another person's body is not likely to be perceived. The full length of the human figure, with some space around it, is encompassed by a level 60-degree gaze. Personal involvment is increased at a social distance of between four and seven feet. Physical contact between subjects can be made with comparative ease with outstretched arms, but it is not possible to seize or strike the other person. It is conversational distance for casual social gatherings, for people who work together and for impersonal business. Considerable facial detail may be detected, including skin texture and hair condition. It is normally out of the range of breath odors or other body odors and body heat.

The personal distance, of between two-and-one-half and four feet, is within easy hand-shaking distance for two persons, or touching distance with the outstretched arm of one person. It is within a "circle of trust" because it is possible to seize or strike the other person. The fine details of complexion, teeth condition and personal cleanliness can be detected at this distance. Occasionally, breath odor and the use of colognes may also be perceived. At personal distances of one-and-a-half to two-and-a-half feet, bodily contact with others can be avoided, but contact can easily be made by minor extension of the extremities. This is the spacing likely to be adopted by a person waiting on a queue line to purchase a theatre ticket. Personal details of cleanliness and grooming may be readily detected, and some body and breath odors perceived.

Intimate distance, eighteen inches or less, is within the whole range of heightened sensory involvement. The sounds, heat and smell of the other person are all perceived and involuntary body contact may be difficult to avoid. In crowded environments this requires special codes of conduct to signal that there is no intent of unwanted intimacy. In crowded elevators, women may be observed folding their arms and men keeping their hands against

Human Body Buffer Zones

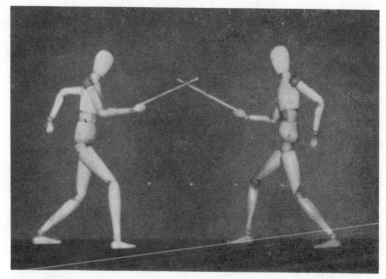

Social distance, or the circle of personal involvement, begins at an inter-person spacing of twelve feet.

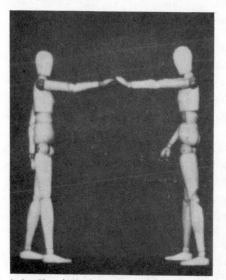 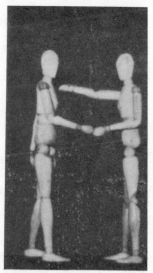

Left—The close phase of social distance, between four to seven feet, is conversational spacing for casual social gatherings and impersonal business.

Right—Personal distance, or the "circle of trust" begins at a spacing of four feet.

their sides. Sight is often distorted, making this distance visually uncomfortable for some persons. Involuntary confrontation and contact at this distance is psychologically disturbing for many persons.

Human buffer zone experiments by psychologists and psychiatrists have confirmed these evaluations of personal space. In one series of experiments, natural personal approach distances were measured between various participants and male and female subjects, both with and without emphasis on personal comfort. In the experiment where the personal comfort criterion was emphasized, participants were instructed that their distance to the subject was to be regulated to the point at which some personal discomfort about the proximity to the subject was experienced. In each of these experiments, approaches from different aspects of the compass were measured, and the resultant buffer zones delineated. In the case where the personal comfort criterion was not emphasized, the buffer zones ranged between 2.4 and 2.8 square feet in area, a slightly larger area than the design ellipse recommended earlier.

Where personal comfort was emphasized, a wider variation in body buffer zones was discovered, with both male and female participants selecting larger inter-person separations from male subjects. The buffer zone around the female subjects ranged between four and five square feet in area, and around male subjects eight to nine square feet. The larger buffer zones selected around the male subjects by both the male and female participants in the experiment were interpreted by psychiatrists as the inherent recognition of potential male aggressiveness. This is in keeping with an "arms reach" separation. As a point of reference, an opened women's umbrella, 30 inches in diameter, covers an area of about five square feet, and an opened men's umbrella, 43 inches in diameter, an area of about ten square feet.

Similar experiments, conducted in a prison, revealed that normal male prisoners would allow an experimenter to approach them up to an approximate radius of 18 inches, or the equivalent of an area zone of seven square feet. Potentially violent, schizophrenic types of prisoners preferred up to four times this area. The larger personal buffer zones selected by abnormal subjects suggests some mental health relationships with crowding. Environmental studies of lower animals have shown detrimental effects due to crowding, but potential human effects remain unknown.

Space Zones in Locomotion

The concept of buffer zones also extends into other human activities. The motorist on the highway establishes a large buffer zone, comprised of his mental image of the extremities of his vehicle, plus the amount of space required for safe stopping of the auto. Penetration of this zone by the cutting in of other motorists is strongly resented. Similarly, normal human locomotion requires larger zones than were observed for the less dynamic situations described in the previous section. This characteristic was aptly described by one of the astronauts, when he stated that the lunar walk still required him to "think two paces ahead, just like walking on Earth."

The space required for locomotion may be divided into a **pacing zone**, the area required for foot placement, and the **sensory zone**, the area required by the pedestrian for perception, evaluation and reaction. The length of the pacing zone is dependent on the age, sex and physical condition of the pedestrian, and has been shown to have a direct linear relationship with speed. Both the pacing and sensory zones can be affected by external influences such as terrain and traffic conditions. Pedestrian pacing lengths may be physically measured, but sensory zone requirements are comprised of many human perceptual and psychological factors.

For reasons of personal safety, or social conventions of avoiding brushing others, or just the joy of sightseeing, the pedestrian is constantly monitoring a whole range of sensory stimuli. His hearing may alert him to a warning automobile horn, his touch to slippery or irregular terrain, his sight to a myriad of visual information, including signs and traffic signals, or collision courses with other pedestrians. These sensory stimuli must be evaluated, and the pedestrian must react in time to avoid danger.

The capabilities of human vision and distance judgement can have a significant effect on pedestrian activities. Gibson, (appendix reference) uses the term "locomotor vision" to describe a whole series of specialized visual characteristics connected with requirements of judging the velocity, distance and direction of others during walking. Somehow pedestrians, through use of vision and their own specialized mental computer, are able to keep track of the varying speeds and angles of oncoming pedestrians and to accurately adjust their pace and speed to avoid collision.

Observations of pedestrians with poorer sight confirms the importance of vision to locomotion. These visually handicapped pedestrians walk more slowly, negotiate stairs more cautiously, and often stop momentarily to get their bearings. The limitations of human vision can even restrict the locomotion of normally sighted persons in some situations. The human eye is capable of detecting very sharp detail within the very small, cone-shaped range of only 3 to 5 degrees. The less acute aspects of detailed vision are possible up to a conical range of about 12 degrees, but, beyond this, vision becomes less detailed, and the comfortable range of general vision is a cone of from 60 to 70 degrees. Pedestrians use the smaller acute cones of vision when caution is required, such as in stair locomotion or when boarding an escalator. In the more general range of comfortable sight capability, it is necessary to be at least seven feet away from another person to observe him from head to toe. This spacing is likely to be adopted in human locomotion at normal walking speeds to avoid stepping on the heels of the person in front.

Reaction time, or time elapsing between visual stimulation and subsequent physical reaction, is an element of the human sensory zone. In controlled studies of automobile braking, it was found that four- to five-tenths of a second elapsed between a visual signal and foot pressure on the brake pedal. This eye-to-foot reaction time increased with age. Reaction times would come into play in human locomotion, and also in the boarding of mechanical aids, such as escalators and moving walks. The slower reaction times of the elderly account in part for their longer boarding times on escalators, which results in reductions in effective escalator capacity. In normal free-speed locomotion, the pedestrian will project a clear zone ahead of him to allow sufficient reaction time to take evasive action.

Walking

Biped walking is a uniquely human skill, which man has evolved into the most efficient means of animal locomotion. Walking has been likened to the human counterpart of the wheel, because of the rolling action of the body's center of gravity and the rotary application of propulsive and supportive forces by the legs and feet. Walking is one of man's most invigorating exercises, stimulating the mind and virtually every muscle of the body, while consuming very little energy. The caloric consumption at normal speed is less than 100 calories per mile, or the equivalent

HUMAN PACING AND SENSORY ZONES

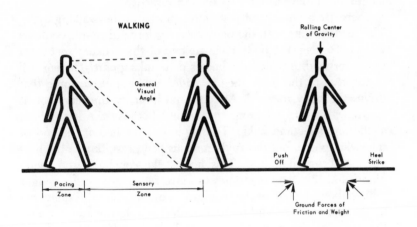

WALKING

General Visual Angle

Rolling Center of Gravity

Push Off

Heel Strike

Pacing Zone

Sensory Zone

Ground Forces of Friction and Weight

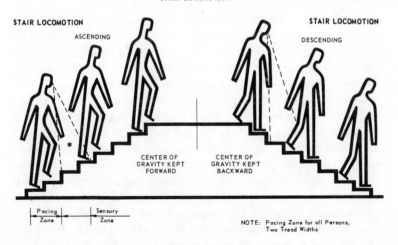

STAIR LOCOMOTION

STAIR LOCOMOTION

ASCENDING

STAIR LOCOMOTION

DESCENDING

CENTER OF GRAVITY KEPT FORWARD

CENTER OF GRAVITY KEPT BACKWARD

Pacing Zone

Sensory Zone

NOTE: Pacing Zone for all Persons, Two Tread Widths

✱ Cone of Greater Visual Acuity

of a 35-mile walk for the weight loss of one pound. Despite its efficiency and apparent ease, walking is a complex mental and kinesthetic activity, taken for granted by all but the handicapped. Walking requires constant shifts in the body's center of gravity to maintain balance, adjustments in the application of foot forces for differences in terrain friction and slope, and adjustments of pacing length and timing to alter speed and direction.

There are a number of distinctive phases in the walking cycle. The stride begins with the body swaying forward to overcome its inertia. To keep the body balance, one of the walker's feet must swing forward to widen the body's pedestal support. The leg still to the rear of the body then provides the propulsive force that drives the body forward. After the push-off by the rear foot, it is swung forward, clearing the ground because the leg is bent at the hip, knee and ankle. The leg is straightened at the end of the swing phase, but the ankle remains bent, resulting in the heel striking the ground first. This heel strike concludes the swing phase, and the body continues to move forward with the weight rolling about the ball of the foot until another push-off is delivered by the rear foot. Ground friction is a factor in locomotion because the force of the push-off is dependent on sufficient opposing frictional force. The horizontal component of foot force at the push-off is about 20 per cent of the body weight, and the heel strike 15 per cent. However, ground friction plays a more important role at the heel strike, because this is the point in the walking cycle when a person is most likely to slip.

The timing and pacing sequence of the walking cycle is thought to be a deeply engraved neurological pattern which is relatively fixed through the greater part of the individual's life span. Experiments based on electrical measurements of the time spacing between foot contacts, and contact duration in the normal human walking pace, have shown a remarkable consistency of gait timing between all ages and sexes. There are differences in other aspects of human walking based on the age and sex of the individual. A familiar feature of the way women walk arises from anatomical differences in the proportions of the male and female pelvis. The smaller range through which the female hip can move backwards and forwards results in a greater pelvic rotation by females for a given length of stride. This aspect of female locomotion has not gone unnoticed by male observers of the passing scene. Aging has the effect of reducing the degree of pelvic rotation for both male and female walkers, reducing the length of stride and thus reduc-

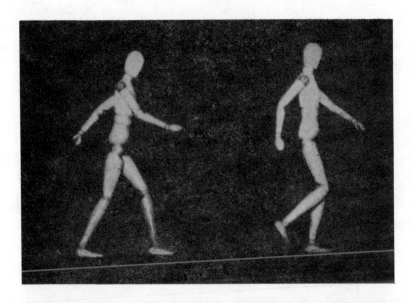

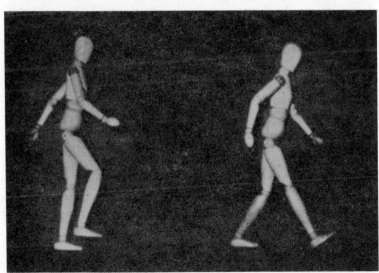

Upper L. to R.—The stride begins with the body swaying forward and the placement of the leading foot; the rear foot provides the push off and is then lifted, with the body-weight moving forward over the leading foot; the rear foot is swung forward clearing the ground because the leg is bent at the hip, knee and ankle, (bottom left); the cycle is completed at the heel strike, with the body continuing to move forward into the next cycle.

ing normal walking speed. Length of stride and pacing rate are determinants of speed, with faster walking characteristically requiring an alteration in the body's center of gravity by effecting a forward stance similar to leaning into the wind.

Detailed photographic observations of male walking patterns have shown a body sway of 4 centimeters (1½ inches) to the left and right during normal locomotion. This sway has not been accurately measured in dense crowds, where human locomotion is restricted to shuffling, but photographic observations show that it is more pronounced, in the range of almost 4 inches to either side. This swaying requirement during restricted locomotion is one of the annoying aspects of walking in a dense crowd, since contact with another pedestrian during the sway causes a momentary loss of balance. Sway measurements have not been made of pedestrians on stairs, but photographic observations indicate a swaying pattern similar to the more restricted locomotion in crowds. Most building codes have assumed working widths of stairs based only on multiples of human shoulder dimensions, without allowance for this swaying factor.

Locomotion on Stairs

Stair climbing and descent is quite different from walking. Locomotion on stairs is necessarily more restricted because of safety considerations, and the restraints imposed by the stair tread and riser configurations. Human energy consumption for climbing stairs is about ten to fifteen times the energy needed for walking the equivalent horizontal distance, and surprisingly, about one-third greater for descent.

When climbing stairs the body's center of gravity is shifted forward, and the front leg is lifted and placed on the first step to support the body and to prevent it from falling forward. Both the front and rear legs provide the push-off, so that the lifting action of both legs is coordinated to provide combined power for ascent. The rear leg is then lifted and swung forward and placed on the second step, and the cycle is repeated. In descending, the center of gravity must be held backward because of the increased danger of falling. Although less energy is required for descent, and speeds of descent are about one-third greater than needed for climbing, greater concentration is required to control the rate by which gravity acts on the body. This requires a careful lowering of the weight to the supporting foot on the step below.

Human Locomotion on Stairs

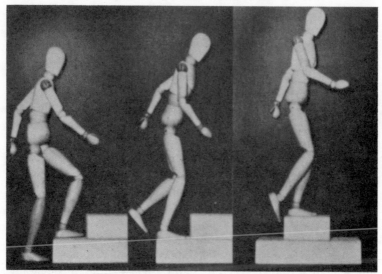

During ascent, the body's center of gravity is shifted forward and the front foot is placed on the first step. Both front and rear legs provide the push-off to raise the body. The rear leg is lifted, swung forward and the foot is placed on the next step.

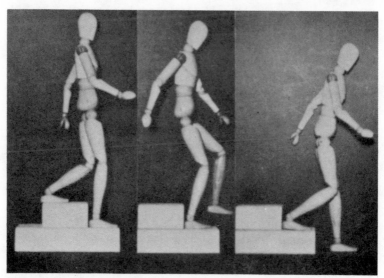

During descent, the body's center of gravity is held backward and the weight is carefully lowered onto the front foot. The rear leg is then lifted, swung forward, and the foot lowered to the next step.

A body sway of about 4 inches occurs as the weight is shifted from foot to foot. As mentioned in the previous section, most building codes have not taken body sway into consideration, specifying stairway widths in multiples of 22 inches, equivalent to the human shoulder breadth. Based on stair locomotion characteristics and observed use of stairs, a 30-inch lane width standard would be more applicable to the dimensioning of narrow stairs.

There are definite shifts in the pacing and sensory characteristics of locomotion on stairs. Instead of selecting a natural pacing distance, the width of the tread determines the pacing distance for all, regardless of physical ability or desired speed. Faster walking is accomplished by increasing the pacing rate and distance, but increased pacing rate is the only way of increasing stair speeds unless stairs are taken two at once, a dangerous and tiring action. Sensory shifts occur on stairs due to the need to use the smaller, more acute cone of vision for more accurate foot placement, and to avoid tripping.

Stair tread, riser, and nosing configurations produce other effects on stair locomotion as well. Many persons with normal walking skill are inconvenienced by stair designs that are incompatible with the bending capabilities of the knee and foot. Handicapped persons experience great difficulty on stairs. Individuals with knee, ankle or hip restrictions, artificial legs, leg braces or crutches are painfully inconvenienced by high riser heights and stairs with projecting nosings which catch the foot. For this reason, the American Standards Specifications for barrier-free building design (A117.1, 1961) recommends a maximum riser height of 7 inches and a rounded nosing flush with the riser, rather than the projecting nosing in common use.

Human energy consumption in stair locomotion has also been found to be related to riser height. A medical research study of energy expenditures using variable treadmill stairs set at angles of 27, 38 and 40 degrees, showed that energy consumption on stairs was more closely correlated with riser height than with tread length, run, diagonal distance or any other single dimension of stair design. In these experiments, a riser height increase of 37.5 per cent, from 6 inches to 8.25 inches, resulted in an increase in energy cost of 96 per cent in ascending, and 58 per cent in descending. Significant increases in pulse rate and blood pressure were also noted with the greater stair angles. From this human factors standpoint, there are many examples of poorly designed stairs. Based on current architectural practice, the range of permissible stair angle design is between 20 and 50 degrees, with the preferred range (by convention) between 30 and 35 degrees. Stair angles below 20 degrees and above 50 degrees are considered dangerous. Structural designers are usually concerned more with designing stairs that fit into the normal bay spacing than with providing a more human design which would require changes in framing dimensions. The survey of stair climbing speeds reported in Chapter Three found that a stair with a 6-inch riser, a 12-inch tread, and a stair angle of 26.5 degrees had more favorable locomotion characteristics and faster pedestrian climbing speeds even though this stair angle is outside the "preferred" architectural range. Additional research is required to determine principles of stair design from the standpoints of the normal human locomotion characteristics, energy consumption, and traffic efficiency.

The Perception of Urban Space

The human perception of large-scale space is a complex process because of the increased role of mental imagery and selectivity. The pedestrian would be helplessly overwhelmed with useless information if every detail of a large space had to be precisely recognized, mentally cataloged, and separately evaluated. A process of selectivity occurs in which secondary visual information is shunted to a level of sub-receptivity, with a concurrent heightening of receptivity to the visual input which is most needed. As an illustration, gas station signs along the highway receive little attention from the driver unless the gas gauge is near empty. Then the receptivity to this particular visual input is increased. If the gas stations are closely spaced, the resulting sense of confidence allows a further increase in receptivity, so that the driver's visual input and selectivity can be expanded to include only stations on the near side of the road, or those selling specific brands. In this limited example, the driver's identification of the visual statement of closely spaced stations increased his confidence and the range of receptivity to added supplementary or secondary information. In a similar manner, the full perception of a large space is closely related to its legibility and clarity of expression. If the visual elements that define the space convey purpose and orientation to the pedestrian, then a wider range of receptivity to other visual inputs is possible. If the visual elements that comprise a space are poorly defined, then a greater degree of concentration is required by the pedestrian to obtain orientation and direction. The required concentration on the specifics of identity and orientation within a poorly defined space, is likely to reduce receptivity and awareness of the aesthetic elements of that space, since aesthetics become a secondary rather than primary information input.

Many of the elements that comprise the human perception of urban space have been defined by Kevin Lynch. (appendix reference) These elements were determined by cataloging the physical compositions of three distinctly different cities, and then questioning the inhabitants about their subjective place images. The components that define urban space were then classified into five broad categories; paths, nodes, landmarks, edges and districts. The **path**, or linkage between nodes, is considered to be the most dominant visual element of space because it is the unifying force upon which the other elements depend. The path provides cohesiveness, identity and the means of expression. While moving along the path, the observer is exposed to the kinesthesia of constantly changing relationships with all the visual elements that comprise the space. Movement enhances the sensory gradients of variations in smell, heat, light, color, texture and gravity, that all combine to produce the total human perception of a space. **Nodes** are the focal points and intersecting junctions of paths and supporting systems such as transit. Direct connections to node points would be a characteristic of a well-defined system. **Landmarks** are statements or points of reference that provide the observer with a continual sense of orientation and relationship with the space. The **edges** are the linear descriptors that define an urban space or district. Edges may be natural linear features, such as a river or lake, or man-made, such as a highway cut or railroad embankment. The configuration of these edges may describe an easily identifiable space entity or district, or it may be so disruptive that no space identity exists. A **district** is an identifiable space entity or precinct with a common identifying character.

The financial district of lower Manhattan derives its identity from the edge elements of the two intersecting rivers on the east and west, and from its many tall buildings. However, the street system of this area causes orientation and identification difficulties for most New Yorkers. The high buildings also limit the use of landmarks for orientation. A clear human identification and image of a space enables one to move freely and confidently through it, in a relaxed manner, with the senses devoted to the full enjoyment of the space. A part of the tourist's visual enjoyment of Paris is obtained from the sense of orientation conveyed by the landmark dominance of the Eiffel Tower supplemented by the juxtaposition of the River Seine.

The sense of orientation conveyed by the Eiffel Tower and the River Seine contribute to the tourist's visual enjoyment of Paris.

Chapter Three
TRAFFIC AND SPACE CHARACTERISTICS
OF PEDESTRIANS

There are many examples of poor, and even hazardous, human environments resulting from a lack of understanding of the traffic-flow relationships and space requirements of pedestrians. A number of authorities have been using maximum pedestrian capacity as a basis for design. Yet, analysis of time-lapse photography of pedestrian traffic flow on walkways and stairs has shown that capacity is reached when there is a dense crowding of pedestrians, causing restricted and uncomfortable locomotion. Insufficient consideration of human space requirements has resulted in inadequate design of many areas where pedestrians may be required to accumulate in large groups. In some instances, overcrowding of these areas has resulted in injury and loss of life.

To meet these inadequacies, this chapter discusses pedestrian traffic volumes and queuing relationships on the basis of average pedestrian area occupancy, providing easily understood measures for design. The chapter also serves as an introduction to the principles used to develop the Level-of-Service Design Standards in Chapter Four, and the illustrative design problems of Chapter Seven.

Some Fundamentals of Traffic Design

Since this text is intended for wide application by members of various design disciplines, a brief discussion of some simple traffic engineering terms and fundamentals is in order. The reader should find sufficient detail in this discussion, and the subsequent illustrative examples of Chapter Seven, to deal with most pedestrian-design problems.

In general, the traffic terms most often used in this text are:
Flow Volume—the number of traffic units passing a point in a unit of time. In pedestrian design, flow is expressed as pedestrians per foot width of the walkway or stairway per minute (PFM). Flow is the most important traffic characteristic, because it determines the width of the pedestrian way (pedway). An inadequate width restricts flow, resulting in pedestrian inconvenience. Volume has been designated as **P**.

Speed—locomotion speed, expressed in distance per unit of time, generally in feet per minute. When related to design of a pedway section, speed is the average speed of all pedestrians passing through the section during the design interval. Speed is designated as **S**.

Density—the number of traffic units per unit of area. In pedestrian design, density would be expressed in tenths of a pedestrian per square foot, a difficult unit to visualize. A more manageable unit, the reciprocal of density, or the square feet of area per pedestrian, is used consistently in this text. The reciprocal of density has been designated as **M**, the Pedestrian Area Module.

Headway—the time and distance separation between traffic units. For example, a two-second headway is the equivalent of one traffic unit passing a point each two seconds, or a flow volume of 30 traffic units per minute. Headway has not been commonly referred to in the design of pedestrian facilities, but it has some useful applications.

Queue—one or more traffic units waiting for service. If the pedway section or service facility has insufficient capacity, a pedestrian queue will develop. Queue lengths and durations will vary according to traffic flow characteristics. In crowded systems, queues may be generated intermittently, due to random variations in traffic intensity.

The flow equation, the classic relationship of traffic design, derived from an analogy to fluid flow in channels, is expressed as follows:

$$\text{Flow Volume} = \text{Average Speed x Average Density}$$
$$\text{or, } P = S \times D$$

As mentioned in the definition of terms, application of the term "density" to pedestrian traffic results in the unwieldy unit of tenths of a pedestrian per square foot, so that the reciprocal of density, square feet area per pedestrian, (**M**), is more useful. This unit also enables us to relate pedestrian flow space to the human factors discussions of the previous chapter, thus producing a clearer concept of design quality. The equation for pedestrian flow volume, (**P**), in pedestrians per foot width of pedway section, per minute, (**PFM**) is expressed as follows:

38

$$\text{Ped Volume} = \frac{\text{Average Ped Speed, feet per minute}}{\text{Average Ped Area, Square feet per ped}}$$

$$\text{or, } P = \frac{S}{M}$$

In this form the designer has a clearer concept of relative design quality, since the units are easier to understand and manipulate. For example, the next section will show that a nearly normal average walking speed of 250 feet per minute is attained with an approximate average pedestrian area of 25 square feet per person, so that the simple division of area occupancy into average speed gives an equivalent design volume of 10 pedestrians per foot width of walkway, per minute.

Time and distance headways can be determined from flow volumes by assuming a specific pedestrian lane width. For example, if a 3-foot pedestrian lane width has a flow volume of 10 PFM, as cited above, this is equal to a pedestrian volume per lane of 30 persons per minute, or the equivalent of an average time-spacing of two seconds between pedestrians. This time-spacing is translated into an average distance-spacing of about 8 feet between following pedestrians, by multiplying by the 250-foot-per-minute walking speed. This time and distance headway separation gives some further visualization of pedway design quality, and is useful for a clearer understanding of the design of entrances.

Walking Speeds

When unimpeded by crowd density or other traffic frictions, pedestrians may vary their walking speeds over a wide range. Figure 3.1 illustrates the distribution of free-flow walking speeds obtained in surveys of about 1000 non-baggage-carrying pedestrians inside the Port Authority Bus Terminal and Pennsylvania Station in New York City. On the basis of these surveys, average free-flow walking speed for all males, females, and the combination of all pedestrians in the surveys, were 270, 254, and 265 feet per minute, respectively. Average speeds were found to decline with age, but individual slow and fast walkers were observed in all age groups.

250 used on p. 110. for moving walks.

250 ft/min = 4.2 fps = 3 mph.

39

PEDESTRIAN WALKING SPEEDS
Unimpeded Free Flow

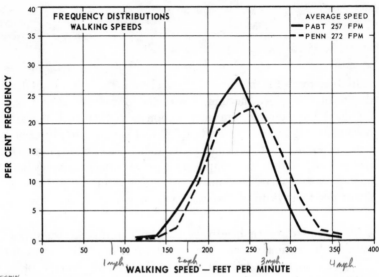

Figure 3.1

528 $\approx$ 88fps = 60 mph.

528 fpm = 6 mph

264 - 3   3 mph.

88 - 1   1 mph

176 - 2

352

Assuming the results of the two pedestrian surveys were representative of the normal population distribution, a statistical inference may be drawn that almost all pedestrians have free-flow walking speeds faster than 145 feet per minute, and that speeds below this level constitute restricted, shuffling human locomotion, and not normal walking. Conversely, the same statistical inference would indicate that walking speeds above 470 feet per minute could be construed as running. As a point of interest, the four-minute mile, near the limit of human performance, equals a speed of 1320 feet per minute.

A controlled study of walking speeds for men, ranging in age from 20 to 87, revealed that normal walking speed declined with age, but that by increasing pacing rates and stride lengths, all participants in the study were capable of exceeding their normal relaxed walking speeds by about forty per cent. This would indicate that a healthy octogenarian in a hurry could exceed the normal relaxed walking speed of a 20-year-old. Normal walking speeds declined from 274 feet per minute for the 20-to-25 age group, to 215 feet per minute for the 81-to-87 group, with most of the speed decline occurring after age 65. Fast walking speeds declined, respectively, from 440 feet per minute to 292 feet per minute, with a similar more pronounced decline after age 65.

Another study of walking speeds in the Pittsburgh Central Business District, showed variances in pedestrian speeds which were correlated with the time of the day, outside temperatures and trip purpose. Pedestrians with restaurant trip purposes were found to have significantly higher speeds than those with business or shopping trip purposes. These studies confirm that there is a great deal of potential variability in individual free-flow walking speeds. Psychological factors, reaction to environment, traffic composition, and trip purpose could all contribute to each pedestrian's selection of his unimpeded free-flow speed.

Surprisingly, such factors as grade, and the presence of baggage or packages, have been found to have no appreciable effect on free-flow walking speed. There were no statistically significant differences in walking speeds due to grades of up to six per cent, according to a survey of walking speeds by age, sex, and grade categories, in the Central Business District of Washington, D. C. Other studies confirm that there is no measurable effect on walking speeds due to grades up to 5 per cent, but that there is a gradual linear decline in speed for steeper grades. A controlled study of soldiers walking on a variable-grade treadmill revealed that an increase in positive treadmill grade, from 5 to 10 per cent, decreased average walking speeds by 11.5 per cent. A further increase in grade to 20 per cent, a slope not normally encountered in most urban areas, decreased normal walking speeds by only 25 per cent. And no statistically significant difference from normal pedestrian walking speeds was shown by a walking speed survey of baggage-carrying pedestrians at the Port Authority Bus Terminal. The lack of effect which hand baggage had on walking speed is confirmed by other research, which found that knapsack weights of up to 25 pounds produced no statistically significant difference in gait.

The remaining, and most significant, determinant of pedestrian walking speed is traffic density. As discussed in the previous chapter, normal walking requires sufficient area for unrestricted pacing, and for sensory recognition and reaction to potential obstacles. As traffic density increases, pedestrian speed is decreased, because of the reduction in available clear area for locomotion. As a result, all pedestrian speeds tend to have less variability as increased crowd density restricts the ability to bypass slower-moving pedestrians, and to select their desired walking

PEDESTRIAN SPEED ON WALKWAYS
Traffic Impeded — One Way Flow

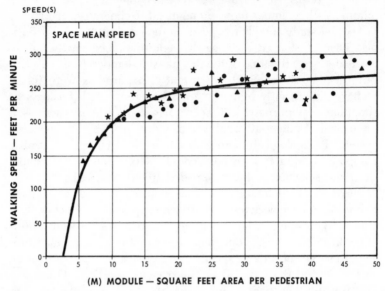

Figure 3.2

speed. Psychological studies of pedestrian behavior have shown that pedestrian interactions, such as eye contact, speed and direction tracking, and evasive maneuvering, occur at inter-person distances of up to 25 feet, with average pedestrian area occupancies as high as 250 square feet per person. However, traffic density has relatively little impact on individual walking speed until an average pedestrian area occupancy of about 40 square feet per pedestrian. The results of a time-lapse photography analysis of pedestrian flow, illustrated in Figure 3.2, shows the effect of increased traffic density, or decreasing area occupancy, on pedestrian walking speeds for one-directional commuter traffic flow. Similar studies of two-directional commuter and multi-directional shoppers' flows resulted in only small variations from this curve, confirming its more general applicability.

The walking-speed curve indicates that mean speeds for dense pedestrian flows are approximately normal, up to an average pedestrian area occupancy of 25 square feet. After this point, walking speed declines rapidly as the available clear area for locomotion decreases. The limit of normal walking speed, established somewhere in the range of 140 to 150 feet per minute, is reached at an area occupancy of about 7 square feet per person. Beyond this point, pedestrians are forced into a restricted and uncomfortable shuffling gait. Walking speed approaches zero at an area occupancy of slightly less than 3 square feet, representative of a crowded, immobile queue.

Traffic Flows on Walkways

Pedestrian volume, or the number of persons passing a given point in a unit of time, is the most important walkway design parameter. If traffic demand exceeds the capacity of a walkway section, crowding, uncomfortable shuffling locomotion and delay will result, producing a poor pedestrian environment. A favorable environment is created if the walkway section is sufficiently wide to allow for normal walking convenience and avoidance of conflicts during all the expected fluctuations in traffic demand.

The previous section showed that normal free walking speed increases as more area is available for locomotion. Average pedestrian areas beyond 25 square feet per person were required before near-normal, free-flow walking speeds could be attained. Pedestrian traffic volume, on the other hand, is inversely proportional to pedestrian area occupancy. Flow volume increases as pedestrian area decreases, until reaching a critical point where locomotion becomes so restricted due to lack of space, that flow volumes begin to decline. Many designers have been using this maximum flow volume, which occurs at or near this critical pedestrian area occupancy, as a basis for design. This produces a limited walkway section that restricts normal locomotion, one which is susceptible to intermittent interruptions and stoppages with normal fluctuations in traffic demand.

Time-lapse photography studies of pedestrian traffic flow on walkways have established flow-volume relationships for the three categories of pedestrian traffic shown in Figure 3.3. These relationships, representing the average conditions of three distinctive types of pedestrian traffic, show a relatively small range of variation, which strongly suggests that reverse and cross-flow traffic conflicts do not drastically reduce either pedestrian traffic volume or speed. This characteristic makes these curves applicable to a wider range of different design conditions.

The adaptability of the pedestrian to minor traffic friction has been noted in other research. A minor traffic flow proportion of 10 per cent of the total flow resulted in only a 14.5 per cent re-

PEDESTRIAN FLOW VOLUME AND AREA
OCCUPANCY ON WALKWAYS

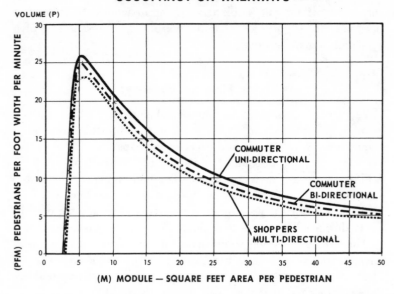

Figure 3.3

duction in potential sidewalk capacity, in a photographic study of university student traffic on sidewalks. As the minor traffic flow proportion increased, its detrimental effect on capacity was actually reduced. With a 50/50 traffic-flow mix, the two-way traffic capacity of the sidewalk was about equal to its one-way capacity. This equalizing effect is due to the fact that smaller-volume reverse-traffic flows are dominated by the larger major flows, forcing the pedestrian moving up-stream to dodge and weave through the oncoming horde. This reduces the traffic efficiency of the section. But as the minor upstream flow gets larger, this one-way domination is reduced, and the walkway section receives more balanced usage. The ease of reverse-flow movement for the minor traffic direction is one measure of the environmental quality of a walkway section. A finding worth noting in the sidewalk study is that pedestrians tend to keep 1- to 1½-foot lateral clear distance between themselves and the curbline. Other observers have noted this pedestrian spacing characteristic adjacent to building lines and along the edges of passageways. This suggests that this lateral distance should be deducted from the walkway dimension when determining effective walkway width.

44

The maximum average peak flow volumes of 26.2, 24.7 and 23.3 persons per foot of walkway width per minute (PFM), shown in Figure 3.3, are representative of design values in use by a number of authorities. Studies of pedestrian flows conducted to determine recommended design standards for civil defense shelter entrances concluded that flows of 20 PFM were attainable under a wide variety of conditions, 25 PFM was attainable under favorable conditions, and that 30 PFM was attainable only under the most favorable walkway conditions and traffic composition. Favorable walkway conditions were defined as a level, paved walkway, whose upstream width was greater than the shelter entrance. Favorable traffic requirements included no interference from conflicting pedestrian or vehicular flows, a minimum number of disabled or infirm persons, only lightweight, hand-carried items of small bulk, and the exercise of control to preclude disorder and panic. Reportedly, marching soldiers in precise military formation, each occupying about 6 square feet, can attain flows of 48 pedestrians per foot per minute for the width of the formation. However, normal pedestrian flows cannot maintain the precise cadence and area occupancy required to attain this flow on a sustained basis. A number of researchers have recorded high surge flows for short periods, under special flow conditions. The civil defense shelter entrance study recorded a 15-second surge flow of 44.7 PFM, within one 5-minute period that averaged about 32 PFM. These high surge rates were observed after a matinee performance at an auditorium, and were attributed to both the greater youth of most of the pedestrians and a sense of urgency to "beat the crowd" to the parking lot.

The extraordinary surge flow of 80 PFM occurred for a short period during a series of experiments conducted in Germany to determine the "ultimate" capacity of a walkway. During this series of experiments, pedestrians flowed through a funnel-like corridor under pressure from the rear, to create dense crowding combined with fast walking speeds. The extraordinary peak performance was obtained after the pedestrians became acclimated to the dense conditions, and adopted a practice of placing their hands on the shoulders of the pedestrian in front. This practice established a uniform space between pedestrians, and allowed the following pedestrian to sense the correct speed and pace from his tactile contact with the pedestrian in front, rather than relying on the normal but slower vision-and-foot reaction process. During the experiment, walking speeds ranged from 250 to 270 feet per minute, at area occupancies as low as 3 square feet per person. Locomotion was observed to be quite abnormal, and it was characterized as a fast "tripping" gait.

While this extreme experiment would appear to have little value for the design of pedestrian spaces, it does suggest that in emergency situations greater pedestrian capacities could be obtained by having following pedestrians placing their hands on the shoulders of the person in front. In times of potential panic, such as might exist when evacuating a building or filling a defense shelter, this procedure would not only produce more efficient flow, but would appear also to establish a better psychological climate. The procedure is recommended for fire drills in schools, to reduce the time needed to evacuate the building in emergencies.

All these extreme variations in flow can be attributed to the infinite flexibility of the human animal, and to his ability to adapt his locomotive skills to a large number of situations. Since the designer is more concerned with the qualitative aspects of the design of walkways, his attention should be directed to the human requirements for space, not only in terms of the area available for normal locomotion, but in terms of the pedestrian's visual and psychological interaction with his environment. All the extreme values of "capacity" which have been cited were obtained at very low personal area occupancies, under psychological pressures and anxiety of varying degrees. The maximum average capacities shown in Figure 3.3 were attained at average pedestrian area occupancies of about 5 square feet per person. This is insufficient area for normal locomotion, and is hardly enough to allow the pedestrian to interact with the surrounding environment. At this close spacing the pedestrian's full sensory awareness must be devoted to the task of restrained locomotion and the avoidance of the pedestrian ahead. This requires complete concentration on pace timing and foot placement, and the use of the smaller and more confined acute range of human vision. The acute range of vision limits visual perceptions to short lines of sight and magnified detail. The perceptive differences in this sensory shift may be compared to viewing a painting so closely that the brush marks destroy the composition and visual impressions intended by the artist. The desirable pedestrian environment allows sufficient space for the pedestrian to choose, independently, his own relaxed walking speed, to bypass slower pedestrians if desired, to avoid conflicts with oncoming or crossing pedestrians, and to interact visually with his surroundings, using the full range of his visual capabilities.

Pedestrian Spacing and Conflicts

The previous two sections have established the relationships of walking speed and flow volumes to average pedestrian area occupancy. The ability to select near-normal walking speed, a qualitative measure of pedestrian flow, was found to require average areas of 25 square feet per person or more. However, other measures are required in order to obtain a clearer understanding of walkway quality. Pedestrians must leave additional space for maneuvering within the traffic stream to bypass slower-moving pedestrians, and to avoid oncoming and crossing pedestrians. This additional space is required to sense the speed and direction of others, and to react without conflict or hesitation.

The spacing of pedestrians in a traffic stream is naturally a function of density. As density increases, pedestrians are forced to maintain constrained spacing patterns to allow for pacing room, and to avoid brushing against others.

Figure 3.4 is a graphic representation of longitudinal and lateral spacings of pedestrians, compiled from analysis of a series of time-lapse photographs. These measurements were restricted somewhat by the dimensional limitations of the photographic field, but it was found that beyond an average area occupancy of 25 square feet per person, spacing patterns were less regular and susceptible to curve fitting. The curves show that in denser traffic conditions pedestrians are more likely to close their ranks by reducing their longitudinal spacing, rather than lateral spacing, which might bring brushing contact with other pedestrians. Contact can cause loss of balance. There are times during the walking cycle when the pedestrian has been said to be "teetering on the brink of falling flat on his face," and any disruption of the center of gravity at these times can quite easily upset the sense of balance. The spacing measurements suggest that average pedestrian areas greater than 25 square feet per person are needed before there is enough lateral space to freely bypass slower-moving pedestrians. Although restricted passing could be accomplished at areas lower than this, it would require the passing pedestrian to turn his body sideways in the minimum profile position described in Chapter Two.

Another aspect of typical pedestrian interaction on walkways is the possibility of conflicts with pedestrians crossing the main-stream of flow. An investigation of pedestrian crossing conflicts was conducted by positioning a time-lapse camera above a location where

47

AVERAGE LONGITUDINAL AND LATERAL SPACING
OF PEDESTRIANS IN A TRAFFIC STREAM
(One Way Flow)

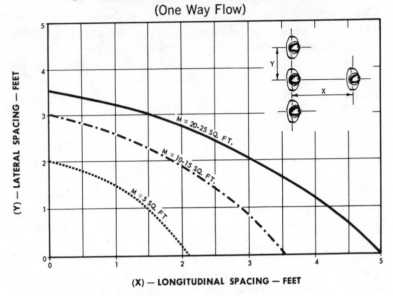

Figure 3.4

pedestrians occasionally cross a main traffic stream at right angles. Crossing movements at various levels of traffic density were observed, and conflicts were recorded. For the purposes of the investigation, a conflict was defined as any stopping and shuffling, or breaking of the normal walking pace, due to a too-close confrontation with another pedestrian. These confrontations required immediate adjustments in speed and direction to avoid collisions.

Pedestrian conflicts are obviously a function of walking speed and pedestrian spacing in the traffic stream. Although wider pedestrian spacings provide larger crossing gaps, the corresponding increase in pedestrian speed tends to continue to make crossing the main-stream difficult. The study results shown in Figure 3.5 indicate that the probability of conflicts due to crossing main-stream traffic exist over a wide range of pedestrian densities. The probability of pedestrian conflict is 100 per cent at 15 square feet

CROSS FLOW TRAFFIC
PROBABILITY OF CONFLICTS

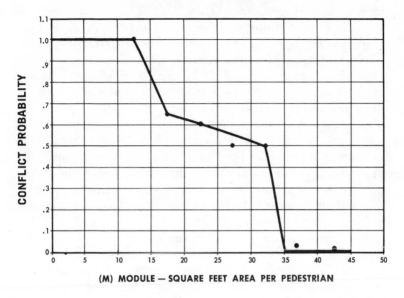

Figure 3.5

per person, representing the absence of acceptable crossing gaps in the main-stream traffic flow. This area occupancy also corresponds with the region of restricted walking speeds and closing of ranks shown by the pedestrian speed and spacing studies. Beyond a pedestrian area of 15 square feet, there is sharp drop in the probability of conflict, as pedestrian ranks open up. However, there is also a concomitant increase in main-stream walking speed, keeping the probability of conflict above 50 per cent until an area of 35 square feet per pedestrian. At this point, the probability of conflict drops sharply, to the zero level. At the 35-square-foot area, sufficient space is available for main-stream and cross-stream pedestrians to react in time to avoid conflicts with each other. The lower probabilities of conflict associated with higher pedestrian areas would be consistent with higher levels-of-service and convenience.

Some interesting photographs illustrating pedestrian crossing interactions at various traffic densities were obtained from this investigation (Figure 3.6). They illustrate the phenomena of tracking speed and direction that occurs between individual pedestrians. The upper photo represents the relatively free traffic flow at 40 square feet per pedestrian, where conflicts can be avoided by minor adjustments in pace or direction. Note the angle of the head of the pedestrian in the center of this photo, indicative of his tracking the crossing pedestrian. In the middle photo, taken at a concentration of 20 square feet per person, this same tracking position of the head can be observed on the crossing pedestrian approaching from the right. The greater probability of potential conflict is also more obvious in this photo. The bottom photo, taken at an area of about 15 square feet per pedestrian, illustrates the greater difficulty and inevitable conflict involved in crossing a traffic stream at this density.

In the next chapter, the qualitative characteristics of pedestrian flow at various traffic concentrations is evaluated and developed into a series of "level-of-service" design standards. The qualitative evaluation includes the ability to select normal walking speed, the freedom to maneuver within the traffic stream and bypass slower pedestrians, and the ability to avoid conflicts with reverse-flow and cross-flow traffic movements.

Entrances

Entrances are, in effect, walkway sections in which pedestrians have been channelized into equal, door-width traffic lanes. In addition to imposing restricted lateral spacing in the traffic stream, entrances may require the pedestrian to perform some time-consuming function such as opening a door or turnstile. The earlier discussion of headways introduced the concept that pedestrians have different average time and distance separations in a traffic stream, dependent on the flow-volume through the design section. This concept is a useful one for evaluating the design of doors, turnstiles and other entrance devices. When a pedestrian opens a door, there must be a sufficient time-headway separation between that pedestrian and the following pedestrian, to allow for the performance of this function. If the time-headway is too close, the following pedestrian reaches the door before the door-opening function is completed, and a growing pedestrian queue will develop. As with walkway flow, doorway systems designed

ILLUSTRATIONS OF CROSSING CONFLICTS

AVERAGE PEDESTRIAN
AREA OCCUPANCY
40 SQ. FT./PED.

AVERAGE PEDESTRIAN
AREA OCCUPANCY
20 SQ. FT./PED.

AVERAGE PEDESTRIAN
AREA OCCUPANCY
15 SQ. FT./PED.

Figure 3.6

at or near maximum capacity are likely to generate frequent queuing and offer a poor level-of-service. Because of the added time required for the door-opening function, entrances will be the weak links in the pedway system, and therefore require added design consideration.

By assuming a traffic lane equal to the entrance width, (see Fundamentals of Traffic Design), the designer can translate pedestrian traffic volumes into time-headway separations. These headways can then be compared with pedestrian performance times for using similar entrance devices. Naturally, different entrance devices have different opening times, and each person will have varying degrees of skill in using these devices. The elderly, the physically handicapped, or those encumbered by packages or baggage, will require longer door opening times.

Turnstiles and doors are weak links in the pedway system, because of the added time required to perform the opening function.

OBSERVED ENTRANCE HEADWAYS

TYPE OF DEVICE	OBSERVED AVERAGE HEADWAY (Seconds)	EQUIVALENT PEDESTRIAN VOLUME (Persons per minute)
Doors		
Free-swinging	1.0 – 1.5	40 – 60
Revolving—one direction	1.7 – 2.4	25 – 35
Registering Turnstiles		
Free Admission	1.0 – 1.5	40 – 60
With Ticket Collector	1.7 – 2.4	25 – 35
Coin-Operated (low)		
Single slot	1.2 – 2.4	25 – 50
Double slot	2.5 – 4.0	15 – 25
Boarding Buses		
Single Coin Fare	2 – 3	20 – 30
Odd Cash Fares	3 – 4	15 – 20
Multi-Zone Fares	4 – 6	10 – 15

Table 3-A

Table 3-A summarizes observed average headways for a number of entrance devices and portal-like situations. While this summary is useful for comparison purposes, the designer is encouraged to examine entrance design problems from the standpoint of traffic headways. This provides a more qualitative insight into system adequacy and level-of-service.

Speed of Locomotion on Stairs

Locomotion on stairs is much more stylized and restricted than walking, because the dimensions of the stairs themselves tend to determine many of the aspects of locomotion that the pedestrian may more freely choose on a level surface. The pacing distance is imposed by the length of the stair tread. The pacing rate may be freely adjusted, but because of greater energy requirements and concerns for safety connected with stair locomotion, this is also limited. The increased attention required for foot placement and maintenance of balance also requires the use of the more acute cones of vision, and for some persons, the supplementary assistance of railings. Stair dimensioning and configuration are important elements of building design which have received very little attention, despite the greater demands on human energy, concerns for safety, and more unusual traffic characteristics of stairs. Speeds of locomotion on stairs have a close relationship to riser height, with the faster speeds, in both ascending and descending directions, occurring on stairs with lower riser heights. As with walking speeds on a level surface, pedestrian speeds on stairs vary with age and sex, but certain characteristics of the distribution of stair speeds, particularly in the down direction, point toward the greater concerns for safety and the influence of handicaps. Figures 3.7 and 3.8 illustrate the results of two stair-speed surveys, one conducted at a stair with a 7-inch riser, 11.25-inch tread, and 32-degree angle, and the other at a stair with a 6-inch riser, 12-inch tread, and 27-degree angle. The figures show the slope, or hypothenuse speed. The down speed distribution exhibits a bi-modality that suggests the presence of two distinctive types of stair users in the descending category, one generally slower than the other. This slower group would be characterized as having a greater concern for safety, and is representative of the segment of the population that has handicaps in varying degrees. The faster group would be, in general, less handicapped, and willing to take chances by using the extra influence of gravity in the descending direction. A summation of the results of two surveys, which involved almost 700 pedestrians, is tabulated by differences in direction, stair angle, sex, and age, in Table 3-B.

PEDESTRIAN SPEEDS ON STAIRS
Unimpeded Free-Flow

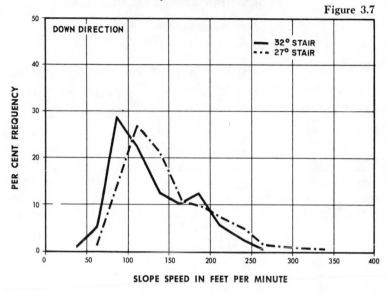

Figure 3.7

DOWN DIRECTION

— 32° STAIR
-·- 27° STAIR

PER CENT FREQUENCY

SLOPE SPEED IN FEET PER MINUTE

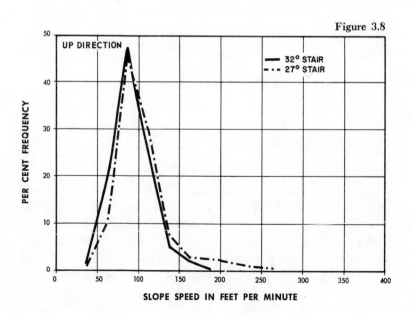

Figure 3.8

UP DIRECTION

— 32° STAIR
-·- 27° STAIR

PER CENT FREQUENCY

SLOPE SPEED IN FEET PER MINUTE

Table 3-B

PEDESTRIAN STAIR SPEEDS

Horizontal Time-Mean-Speeds
(Feet Per Minute)

	DOWN DIRECTION		UP DIRECTION	
	(1)	(2)	(1)	(2)
Age—29 or under				
Males	163	183	110	120
Females	117	132	106	110
Group Average	149	160	108	115
Age—30 to 50				
Males	136	160	101	116
Females	100	128	94	107
Group Average	127	153	99	114
Age—Over 50				
Males	112	118	85	81
Females	93	111	77	89
Group Average	108	117	83	83
Average—all ages, sexes	132	152	100	113

(1) Indoor stair, 7-inch riser, 11.25-inch tread, 32-degree angle
(2) Outdoor stair, 6-inch riser, 12.0-inch tread, 27-degree angle

The speeds shown in this tabulation are based on the horizontal component, or the level equivalent speed, to provide a basis for comparison with walking speeds. More importantly, this equivalent level, or horizontal speed, is required mathematically to make the pedestrian flow-density equation applicable to the design of stair widths. You will note that age appears to have a more pronounced effect on stair locomotion speeds, producing a one-third decline in speed within the age groups surveyed. A more significant difference in the speeds of the sexes may also be noted, related to the greater energy requirements of locomotion on stairs. In addition, the lower riser height is seen to result in faster speeds, suggesting that this type of stair would be more efficient from a traffic-flow standpoint as well as being a more "human" stair, because of the greater tread area for foot placement, and the smaller energy consumption of the lower riser height. Surprisingly, the more efficient 27-degree-angle stair is outside the "preferred" range of from 30 to 35 degrees, recommended by architectural handbooks. This is indicative of a need for more understanding of stair design, and its relationship to the human characteristics of locomotion. Based on the population variations discovered in these two studies, a statistical inference may be drawn that virtually all pedestrians climb stairs faster than the horizontal speed of about 40 feet per minute, and that stair ascent speeds in excess of an approximate horizontal speed of about 165 feet per minute are representative of a running type of ascent. This range is representative of the comfortable, and possibly safe, limit of human locomotion speed on stairs.

Because of the many specialized characteristics of human locomotion on stairs, increased traffic density has less of an effect on pedestrian speed. As long as the pedestrian is assured sufficient lateral spacing for his shoulder-breadth and body-sway requirements, and there are at least two vacant stair-treads ahead, he has about all the space that is needed for normal stair locomotion. This translates to the rather small pedestrian area occupancy of about 7 to 8 square feet per person. However, traffic density produces other effects which bring about a reduction in the average speed of the traffic stream. The more agile pedestrian becomes confined and restricted, and unable to bypass the slower, and often handicapped, pedestrian, thus reducing the total average speed of the group. This restriction is psychologically more frustrating than the comparable situation on walkways, because of the more confined environment of the stair and the need for greater concentration on balance, close vision, and foot placement. Figures 3.9 and 3.10 illustrate the results of time-lapse photography studies of the relationship of pedestrian area occupancy on speed. The photographic studies confirm that approximately normal stair locomotion speeds are attained at an average area occupancy of about ten square feet per person. The

PEDESTRIAN SPEED ON STAIRS
Traffic Impeded — One Way Flow

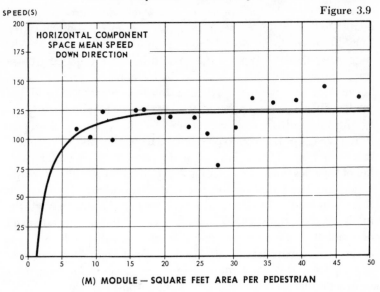

Figure 3.9

SPEED(S)

HORIZONTAL COMPONENT
SPACE MEAN SPEED
DOWN DIRECTION

(M) MODULE — SQUARE FEET AREA PER PEDESTRIAN

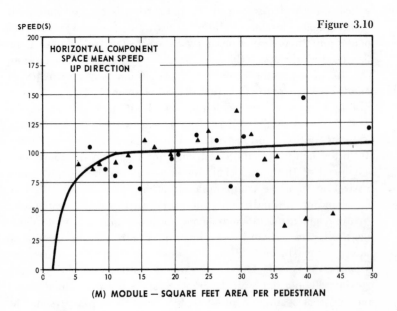

Figure 3.10

SPEED(S)

HORIZONTAL COMPONENT
SPACE MEAN SPEED
UP DIRECTION

(M) MODULE — SQUARE FEET AREA PER PEDESTRIAN

ascending direction is of greater interest to the designer, because the slower speeds and lower volumes of ascent are the controlling design factor. The plot of the ascending direction data shows increasing variability beyond an average area occupancy of 20 square feet per person. This area occupancy can be roughly associated with a lateral spacing of at least four feet between pedestrians, and a longitudinal spacing of at least 5 tread lengths. This would give the pedestrian sufficient area to select his own stair speed, and to bypass slower-moving pedestrians.

Traffic Flow on Stairways

Although greater emphasis on stair dimensioning, and the human aspects of safety and energy consumption, are recommended as part of the qualitative design of stairways, stairway volumes remain as the most significant design parameter. The results of time-lapse photography studies of pedestrian flow on stairs are shown in Figure 3.11 and 3.12. The lower flow volumes of the upward direction are the determinant of stairway width and design quality, and all references to capacity in this section will be confined to the **up** direction, unless otherwise stated.

As with walkway volumes, maximum stairway flow occurs in the region of minimum pedestrian area occupancy, about at the point of a two-tread length and one shoulder breadth area, or approximately three square feet per person. In this confined area, forward progress is determined by movement of the pedestrian ahead. Ascent speeds at this area occupancy are at the lower limit of the normal range shown in the speed studies of the previous section, indicative of an inconvenient and unnatural pace for all pedestrians. The maximum flow volume of 18.9 pedestrians per minute per foot of stairway width is representative of design values used by many authorities. These stairway design values in the capacity region create the most crowded pedestrian environment, with restricted locomotion speeds for almost all persons, and a high probability of developing intermittent stoppages and queuing, with even normal fluctuations in traffic. Studies conducted by the Regional Plan Association of New York disclosed that stair use was reasonably fluid, without queuing, up to about 12 PFM, but beyond this point queuing developed as pedestrian spacing and speed were reduced. This value corresponds roughly to the level of normal average stair locomotion speed developed in the previous section. It is also compatible with the area oc-

PEDESTRIAN FLOW VOLUMES AND
AREA OCCUPANCY ON STAIRS

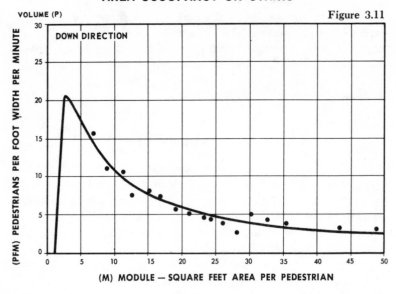

VOLUME (P)   Figure 3.11

(PFM) PEDESTRIANS PER FOOT WIDTH PER MINUTE

DOWN DIRECTION

(M) MODULE — SQUARE FEET AREA PER PEDESTRIAN

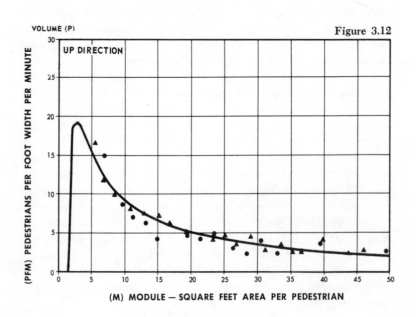

VOLUME (P)   Figure 3.12

(PFM) PEDESTRIANS PER FOOT WIDTH PER MINUTE

UP DIRECTION

(M) MODULE — SQUARE FEET AREA PER PEDESTRIAN

cupancy of about 7 to 8 square feet per person suggested as the minimum area required for normal stair locomotion. While this provides some minimum space and maximum volume criteria, it is not a free-flowing traffic stream where passing and selection of individual speed is possible.

Because of the critical aspects of pedestrian balance in stair locomotion, and the generally narrow widths of stairs, they are less flexible traffic movers than walkways. The deferential side-stepping and maneuvering that occurs on walkways, which tends to make them less sensitive to opposing traffic, does not exist to the same degree on stairs. In addition, because they are generally narrower, or divided by railings, stairway widths are more critical than walkways widths. Unlike walkways, a minor traffic flow on a narrow stair can effectively cut stairway capacity in half, so the designer is cautioned to adjust for directionality of flow in stairway dimensioning. Level-of-service design standards for stairways, based on a qualitative evaluation of stairway flow, are contained in the next chapter.

Minor reverse flows detract significantly from stairway capacity because stairs are not as flexible as walkways.

Pedestrian Queuing

Queuing may be broadly defined as any form of pedestrian waiting that requires standing in a relatively stationary position for some period of time. Queues may be of two general types: a **lineal** or **ordered** queue, with conventional first-come, first-served priority, or a **bulk** queue, which would be unordered, and without an established queue discipline. **Bulk** queuing areas may be divided into those devoted only to standing and waiting, with limited movement within the queuing area, or those devoted to waiting combined with some need for reasonably free internal circulation through the queuing area. Examples of the respective types are illustrated by the photos in Figure 3.13. These photos illustrate a ticket line with an ordered lineal queue; a bulk queue without established order at the foot of a motorstair, and bulk queuing with requirements for internal circulation on a subway platform. There are no known standards for the design of queuing spaces, and this aspect of pedestrian design is often overlooked.

Most pedestrian facilities are designed adequately for moving pedestrians who may have larger, although transient, space demands, but the potential dangers of serious crowding due to temporary disruptions of service, or loss of crowd control, are rarely considered. Crowd pressure has been the cause of a number of fatalities at sports stadiums in Europe and South America, and unless they have personally experienced it, most designers, or even those persons responsible for crowd control, cannot realize the body-crushing forces and potential for panic that can occur. The author was subjected to one such experience, which left a lasting impression and conviction that greater emphasis must be placed on the maximum allowable human occupancy of certain areas. This experience occurred at a major suburban railroad terminal after a snowstorm had disrupted outbound train service. Thousands of stranded passengers gathered in a large but restricted area, at a common entrance to train platforms. The average pedestrian area occupancy was probably about one-and-one-half square feet per person. "Shock" waves ran through the crowd as if it were a single unified mass, literally lifting people off their feet. Police attempting to control the crowd were thrown back by surges which they could not stop, even though they had locked their arms. Although some trains arrived during this period they were inaccessible, because it was impossible for passengers to move through the dense crowd to platform entrances that were as little

CATEGORIES OF PEDESTRIAN QUEUES

LINEAL ORDERED QUEUE

BULK QUEUE — NO CIRCULATION

BULK QUEUE — WITH CIRCULATION

Figure 3.13

as twenty feet away. Fortunately no panic occurred in the situation, but if the scene had been duplicated on the railroad platform, many pedestrians would have been unavoidably forced onto the tracks.

Accumulations of waiting pedestrians, caused by service stoppages or capacity restrictions of any type, are an aspect of design quality that should be carefully evaluated. The pedestrian holding capacity of all public spaces should be known. If potential exists for crowding approaching the limits of human convenience, comfort or safety, alternative designs or operating procedures must be considered. Queuing spaces must be evaluated from the standpoint of their varying degrees of mobility, with consideration of the psychological factors discussed in Chapter Two.

The approximate limit of human occupancy of a confined space is illustrated by the two photos in Figure 3.14, taken during experiments conducted by the Otis Elevator Company to determine the practical capacity of elevators. The upper photo shows all-female occupancy on an elevator at about 1.5 square feet per person, and the lower, mixed occupancy at about 1.8 square feet per person. The persons involved in the experiment are wearing lightweight summer clothing, and are not carrying packages or personal accessories. The lower photograph shows that in a crowded, mixed-occupancy elevator, women will fold their arms, enlarging their area requirements. The photos show clearly that unavoidable bodily contact is experienced by all pedestrians, and that mobility within the confines of the area would be impossible. A survey of persons using an office-building elevator revealed that unavoidable contact with other pedestrians was experienced at an average area of about 2¾ square feet per person. Approximately 3½ square feet per person was required before the elevator was considered to be uncrowded. Elevators represent a special circumstance in which pedestrians are willing to submit to closer spacing than they would normally accept in a free-standing situation, surrounded by strangers. Observations of dense bulk queues, at escalators or crosswalks, show that pedestrian area occupancies will average about 5 square feet per person in these less confined circumstances.

Linear ordered queues, such as those which occur on ticket lines, are remarkably consistent with the spacing observed in psychological experiments. Bus commuters have been found to select inter-person spacings at about 19 to 20 inches, with very little variation, for both ticket purchase and bus waiting lines. Ticket

PEDESTRIAN AREA OCCUPANCY OF ELEVATORS

ALL FEMALE OCCUPANCY — APPROXIMATELY
1.5 SF/PERSON

MIXED OCCUPANCY — APPROXIMATELY
1.8 SF/PERSON

Figure 3.14

line measurements of inter-city bus passengers with baggage showed a very small increase in this spacing, since most of these pedestrians placed their baggage between their feet or at their sides. Based on a normal ticket-selling position spacing of 5 feet, the persons observed in this type of queue occupied 8 to 9 square feet per person. Movement through the queuing area was possible, but on an "excuse me" basis.

The body ellipse discussed in Chapter Two provides a useful method for illustrating queuing densities and synthesizing pedestrian mobility in queuing areas. Figures 3.15, 3.16, 3.17 and 3.18, illustrate various levels of pedestrian area occupancy, assuming uniform inter-person spacing and circular body buffer zones. The assumption of equal inter-person spacing is a rather generous one, and considered valid for the limited range of conditions examined. Figure 3.15 is a simulation of a group of pedestrians equally spaced in individual 2-foot-diameter buffer zones. This assumption results in a queuing area of 3 square feet per person, and could be called the boundary of the **touch-zone,** because below this area occupancy, frequent unavoidable contact between pedestrians is likely to occur. There is no possibility for circulation within this zone, and movement would be restricted to shuffling forward in sequence with those in front. This area occupancy is representative of a slightly crowded elevator, or of the front ranks of a dense escalator or crosswalk queue.

In Figure 3.16, the body buffer zone has been expanded to an inter-person spacing of 3 feet, and a 7-square-foot area. This might be called the boundary of the **no-touch zone,** because contact with others can be avoided between 3 to 7 square feet per person, as long as movement within the queuing area is not necessary. However, movement would be possible as a group, and this restricted spacing is actually within the range of pedestrian area occupancy that produces maximum flow capacity on walkways and stairs.

Figure 3.17 illustrates the expansion of the body buffer zone to a 3½-foot diameter and a 10-square-foot area. This might be termed the boundary of the **personal comfort zone,** since a 7- to 10-square-foot area is within the range of spacial separation and area occupancy that people have selected in experiments emphasizing the comfort criterion. At this spacing, a full body depth separates standees, allowing limited lateral circulation by moving sideways between standing pedestrians. In Figure 3.18, the body

PEDESTRIAN QUEUING SIMULATION

Figure 3.15

12" RADIUS – TOUCH ZONE

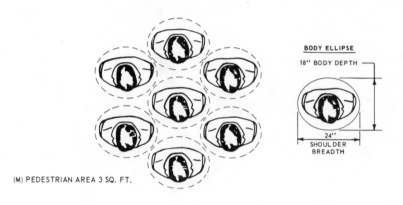

BODY ELLIPSE

18" BODY DEPTH

24"
SHOULDER
BREADTH

(M) PEDESTRIAN AREA 3 SQ. FT.

18" RADIUS – NO TOUCH ZONE

Figure 3.16

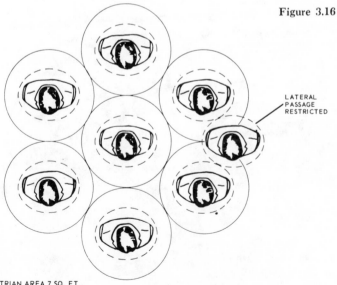

LATERAL
PASSAGE
RESTRICTED

(M) PEDESTRIAN AREA 7 SQ. FT.

PEDESTRIAN QUEUING SIMULATION

Figure 3.17

21" RADIUS – PERSONAL COMFORT ZONE

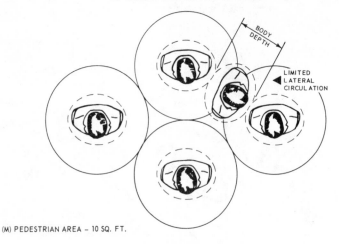

(M) PEDESTRIAN AREA – 10 SQ. FT.

24" RADIUS – CIRCULATION ZONE

Figure 3.18

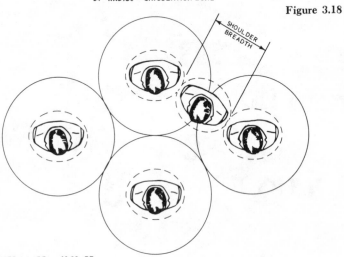

(M) PEDESTRIAN AREA – 13 SQ. FT.

buffer zone has been expanded to a 4-foot diameter and a 13-square-foot area. This might be termed the boundary of the **circulation zone,** since circulation within a queuing area with an average area occupancy of 10 to 13 square feet per person would be possible without disturbing others. The synthesis of queuing space occupancy is the basis of the queuing level-of-service design standards that appear in the next chapter.

Some Notes on Arrival Processes

Arrival processes are an important determinant of the characteristics of use of all pedestrian facilities. The arrival process should be clearly understood by the designer before qualitative design standards are applied. There are two basic types of pedestrian arrival processes: **bulk process** and **intermittent process** arrivals. An example of a **bulk process** arrival pattern occurs after a sporting event, when there is an immediate mass exodus of spectators, or at a railroad terminal platform, when a fully loaded passenger train discharges in a few minutes. Bulk process arrivals temporarily exceed the capacity of pedestrian facilities by the impact of their excessive short-term demands. Facilities subjected to a bulk process arrival pattern always function at the limit of their practical working capacity, regardless of the design assumption, until all arrivals are serviced. The qualitative evaluation of bulk process facilties is based on pedestrian service times and the queuing adequacy of their approach sections. For example, minimum design criteria for a railroad platform subjected to bulk process train arrivals should be clearance of the platform before the next train arrival. Chapter Seven contains an illustrative problem of this type.

Intermittent arrival patterns are characteristic of a typical pedestrian facility such as a large transportation terminal, or office building, served by multiple sources of demand. Intermittent arrival facilities tend to have more regular overall traffic patterns, but are subject to short-term surges, or "micropeaks", of traffic volume considerably higher than the average, or short-term gaps in which traffic volume falls far below the average.

The distinction in arrival processes can be important to the designer, since the assumption of an "average" design period, which is not truly representative of the actual arrival pattern, may produce an inadequate and inconvenient facility.

Chapter Four

Level-of-Service Design Standards

The dimensional design of pedestrian spaces involves the application of traffic engineering principles plus the consideration of human convenience and the design environment. Different environments logically require the application of different qualitative, as well as quantitative, design standards. The pedestrian design rationale for shopping areas would not apply to transportation terminals, and it follows that airport terminal standards would not directly apply to rapid transit facilities. Each has its own traffic patterns, physical restraints, and individual environmental requirements.

The previous chapter emphasized the fact that many authorities are using maximum capacity ratings for dimensioning pedestrian space. No evaluation or consideration of human convenience has been made in developing these design standards. The flow curves of the previous chapter demonstrated that the maximum capacity of a pedestrian traffic stream is attained only when there is a dense crowding of pedestrians. The crowding results in significant reductions in pedestrian convenience as normal human locomotion speeds are restricted, due to a loss of freedom to maneuver within the traffic stream. Since human convenience is a primary consideration in environmental design, pedestrian design standards must be based on a relative scale of this factor.

The Level-of-Service Concept

The Level-of-Service Concept was first developed in the field of traffic engineering in recognition of the fact that capacity design was, in effect, resulting in planned congestion.

The *Highway Capacity Manual*, the most authoritative reference on highway design practice, develops standards for six levels of design, based on service volumes and a qualitative evaluation of driver convenience. This qualitative evaluation includes the freedom to choose desired vehicle operating speed, the ability to overtake and pass other vehicles, and the freedom to change lanes. The Level-of-Service concept provides a useful model for the design of pedestrian spaces as well. Pedestrian service standards should, similarly, be based on the freedom to select normal locomotion speed, the ability to bypass slow-moving pedestrians, and the relative ease of cross-and reverse-flow movements at various pedestrian traffic concentrations.

Level-of-Service standards provide the designer with a useful means of determining the environmental quality of a pedestrian space, but they are no substitute for judgement. The designer must examine all elements of pedway design, including such traffic characteristics as the magnitude and duration of peaks, surging or platooning caused by traffic light cycles or transit arrivals, and all the economic ramifications of space utilization. When designing for extreme peak demands of short duration, the designer may apply a lower quality level-of-service standard to obtain a more economical design. However, caution must be exercised in selecting design standards near maximum capacity levels, since the critical pedestrian density at these levels is likely to be exceeded intermittently. This would cause flow volumes to actually fall below the specified design level, resulting in pedestrian delay and crowding. When the designer is required to use maximum capacity volumes, such as in sports stadium design, he must examine the adequacy of holding areas at the approaches to the critical section. In such situations, pedestrian waiting and system-clearance times should form the basis for the qualitative evaluation of the design.

The level-of-service standards in the remainder of the chapter are based on a range of pedestrian area occupancies. Design volumes for walkways and stairways are also presented as a range. If traffic is comprised of commuters or workers, then the higher design volumes in a given range may be assumed. The lower range of design volumes would be recommended if traffic is comprised largely of shoppers, persons carrying baggage, or if there are conflicting traffic movements. Walkway and stairway levels-of-service are illustrated by photographs of one-directional flow at the approximate pedestrian area occupancy representing that service level. The photographs are supplemented by a written description of the qualitative aspects of each level-of-service. Design applications for the various service standards are presented in Chapter Seven.

Walkway Standards

The breakpoints that determine the various levels-of-service have been determined on the basis of the walking speed, pedestrian spacing, and the probabilities of conflict at various traffic concentrations developed in the previous chapter. The standards provide the means of determining the design quality of corridors, sidewalks and entranceways. The effective width of corridors must be reduced by 18 inches on each corridor side, to take into account the human propensity to maintain this separation from stationary objects and walls, except under the most crowded conditions. Where there is a tendency for window shopping, net width should be reduced by an additional 18 inches, to allow for standing pedestrians. When designing sidewalks, the effective walkway width must be reduced by an additional 2 feet, or more, to take into account the constricting effects of street impedimenta such as parking meters, light standards, fire hydrants and refuse cans. The effects of larger individual obstructions, such as newsstands or subway stairs, should also be evaluated, particularly when they are placed at the critical crosswalk section. Traffic signal cycles, or transit arrivals, have a tendency to concentrate flow into platoons and surges of denser traffic, and this effect should also be considered when applying the service standards.

The walkway standards are operative within a definitive range of flow for which meaningful relationships have been observed. Beyond this range, pedestrian flow tends to become slightly erratic and less defined. This does not detract from the value of the standards. While they are a substantial departure from previous design assumptions, they are still representative of a "busy" situation. For example, when used on an hourly basis, the highest service standard may equal a flow of as many as 4000 persons per hour on a 15-foot sidewalk, with a net effective walkway width of 10 feet. The designer is therefore encouraged to deal with shorter peak periods, and surges within the peak, to determine representative walkway quality. When designing sidewalks, the designer should particularly address himself to the adequacy of the critical crosswalk area, with its multi-directional flows, conflicts with turning vehicles, and space requirements for standing pedestrians. This area is also a prime location for walkway impedimenta.

Photographic illustrations and descriptions of walkway levels-of-service are shown on the following pages. Pedestrian flow volume and area relationships are shown on the curve in Fig. 4.1.

LEVEL-OF-SERVICE DESCRIPTIONS FOR WALKWAYS
Level of Service A

Average Pedestrian Area Occupancy: 35 square feet per person, or greater.
Average Flow Volume: 7 PFM, or less. *

At walkway level-of-service A, sufficient area is provided for pedestrians to freely select their own walking speed, to bypass slower pedestrians, and to avoid crossing conflicts with others. Designs consistent with this level-of-service would include public buildings or plazas without severe peaking characteristics or space restrictions.

Level of Service B

Average Pedestrian Area Occupancy: 25-35 square feet per person.
Average Flow Volume: 7-10 PFM.

At walkway level-of-service B, sufficient space is available to select normal walking speed, and to bypass other pedestrians in primarily one-directional flows. Where reverse-direction or pedestrian crossing movements exist, minor conflicts will occur, slightly lowering mean pedestrian speeds and potential volumes. Designs consistent with this level-of-service would be of reasonably high type, for transportation terminals and buildings in which recurrent, but not severe, peaks are likely to occur.

Level of Service C

Average Pedestrian Area Occupancy: 15-25 square feet per person.
Average Flow Volume: 10-15 PFM.

At walkway level-of-service C, freedom to select individual walking speed and freely pass other pedestrians is restricted. Where pedestrian cross movements and reverse flows exist, there is a high probability of conflict requiring frequent adjustment of speed and direction to avoid contact. Designs consistent with this level-of-service would represent reasonably fluid flow; however, considerable friction and interaction between pedestrians is likely to occur, particularly in multi-directional flow situations. Examples of this type of design would be heavily used transportation terminals, public buildings, or open spaces where severe peaking, combined with space restrictions, limit design flexibility.

*PFM = Pedestrians per foot width of walkway, per minute.

LEVEL OF SERVICE ILLUSTRATIONS FOR WALKWAYS

Level of Service A

Level of Service B

Level of Service C

Level of Service D

Average Pedestrian Area Occupancy: 10-15 square feet per person.
Average Flow Volume: 15-20 PFM.

At walkway level-of-service D, the majority of persons would have their normal walking speeds restricted and reduced, due to difficulties in bypassing slower-moving pedestrians and avoiding conflicts. Pedestrians involved in reverse-flow and crossing movements would be severely restricted, with the occurrence of multiple conflicts with others. Designs at this level-of-service would be representative of the most crowded public areas, where it is necessary to continually alter walking stride and direction to maintain reasonable forward progress. At this level-of-service there is some probability of intermittently reaching critical density, causing momentary stoppages of flow. Designs consistent with this level-of-service would represent only the most crowded public areas.

Level of Service E

Average Pedestrian Area Occupancy: 5-10 square feet per person.
Average Flow Volume: 20-25 PFM.

At walkway level-of-service E, virtually all pedestrians would have their normal walking speeds restricted, requiring frequent adjustments of gait. At the lower end of the range, forward progress would only be made by shuffling. Insufficient area would be available to bypass slower-moving pedestrians. Extreme difficulties would be experienced by pedestrians attempting reverse-flow and cross-flow movements. The design volume approaches the maximum attainable capacity of the walkway, with resulting frequent stoppages and interruptions of flow. This design range should only be employed for short peaks in the most crowded areas. This design level would occur naturally with a bulk arrival traffic pattern that immediately exceeds available capacity, and this is the only design situation for which it would be recommended. Examples would include sports-stadium design, or rail transit facilities where there may be a large but short-term exiting of passengers from a train. When this level-of-service is assumed for these design conditions, the adequacy of pedestrian holding areas at critical design sections, and all supplementary pedestrian facilities, must be carefully evaluated.

Level of Service D

Level of Service E

Level of Service F

Level of Service F

Average Pedestrian Area Occupancy: 5 square feet per person, or less.

Average Flow Volume: Variable, up to 25 PFM.

At walkway level-of-service F, all pedestrian walking speeds are extremely restricted, and forward progress can only be made by shuffling. There would be frequent, unavoidable contact with other pedestrians, and reverse or crossing movements would be virtually impossible. Traffic flow would be sporadic, with forward progress based on the movement of those in front. This level-of-service is representative of a loss of control, and a complete breakdown in traffic flow. Pedestrian areas below 5 square feet are more representative of a queuing, rather than a traffic-flow situation, and this level-of-service is not recommended for walkway design.

LEVEL OF SERVICE STANDARDS FOR WALKWAYS
Volume (P) vs. Module (M)

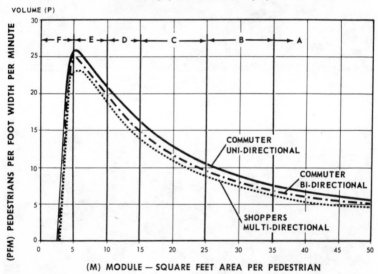

Figure 4.1

Stairway Standards

When designing stairs, increased consideration must be given to the role of human characteristics, because of the greater safety hazards and energy expenditure required in locomotion on stairs. In addition to the exercise of designer judgement in evaluating the traffic patterns and peaking characteristics recommended for use of Walkway Standards, the following factors should be considered in stairway design:

- Stairs should be located so as to be readily visible and identifiable as a means of direct access to the levels they are designed to interconnect;
- Clear areas large enough to allow for queuing pedestrians should be provided at the approaches to all stairways;
- Stairs should be well lighted;
- Stair nosing, riser, tread, and railing configurations should be designed to assist human locomotion, particularly for the handicapped;
- Riser heights should be kept below 7 inches, to reduce energy expenditure and to increase traffic efficiency;
- When a stairway is placed directly within a corridor, the lower capacity of the stairway is the controlling factor in the design of the pedway section;
- Where minor, reverse-flow traffic volumes frequently occur on a stair, the effective width of the stair for the major-direction design flow should be reduced by a minimum of one traffic lane, or 30 inches.

Photographic illustrations and descriptions of the stairway levels-of-service are shown on the following pages. Pedestrian flow volume and area relationships are shown in the curve in Figure 4.2.

LEVEL OF SERVICE DESCRIPTIONS FOR STAIRWAYS

Level of Service A

Average Pedestrian Area Occupancy: 20 square feet per person, or greater.
Average Flow Volume: 5 PFM, or less.*

At stairway level-of-service A, sufficient area is provided to freely select locomotion speed, and to bypass other slower-moving pedestrians. No serious difficulties would be experienced with reverse traffic flows. Designs at this level-of-service would be consistent with public buildings or plazas that have no severe traffic peaks or space limitations.

Level of Service B

Average Pedestrian Area Occupancy: 15-20 square feet per person.
Average Flow Volume: 5-7 PFM.

At stairway level-of-service B, representing a space approximately 5 treads long and 3 to 4 feet wide, virtually all persons may freely select locomotion speeds. However, in the lower range of area occupancy, some difficulties would be experienced in passing slower-moving pedestrians. Reverse flows would cause minor traffic conflicts. Designs at this level-of-service would be consistent with transportation terminals, and public buildings that have recurrent peak demands and no serious space limitations.

Level of Service C

Average Pedestrian Area Occupancy: 10-15 square feet per person.
Average Flow Volume: 7-10 PFM.

At stairway level-of-service C, representing a space approximately 4 to 5 treads long and about 3 feet wide, locomotion speeds would be restricted slightly, due to an inability to pass slower-moving pedestrians. Minor reverse-traffic flows would encounter some difficulties. Design at this level-of-service would be consistent with transportation terminals, and public buildings with recurrent peak demands and some space restrictions.

*PFM = Pedestrians per foot width of stairway, per minute.

LEVEL OF SERVICE ILLUSTRATIONS FOR STAIRWAYS

Level
of
Service

A

B

C

LEVEL OF SERVICE DESCRIPTIONS FOR STAIRWAYS

Level of Service D

Average Pedestrian Area Occupancy: 7-10 square feet per person.
Average Flow Volume: 10-13 PFM.

At stairway level-of-service D, representing a space approximately 3 to 4 treads long and 2 to 3 feet wide, locomotion speeds are restricted for the majority of persons, due to the limited open tread space and an inability to bypass slower-moving pedestrians. Reverse flows would encounter significant difficulties and traffic conflicts. Designs at this level-of-service would be consistent with the more crowded public buildings and transportation terminals, subjected to relatively severe peak demands.

Level of Service E

Average Pedestrian Area Occupancy: 4-7 square feet per person.
Average Flow Volume: 13-17 PFM.

At stairway level-of-service E, representing a space approximately 2 to 4 tread lengths long and 2 feet wide, the minimum possible area for locomotion on stairs, virtually all persons would have their normal locomotion speeds reduced, because of the minimum tread length space and inability to bypass others. Intermittent stoppages are likely to occur, as the critical pedestrian density is exceeded. Reverse-traffic flows would experience serious conflicts. This level-of-service would only occur naturally with a bulk arrival traffic pattern that immediately exceeds available capacity, and this is the only design situation for which it would be recommended. Examples would include sports stadiums, or transit facilities where there is a large uncontrolled, short-term exodus of pedestrians.

Level of Service F

Average Pedestrian Area Occupancy: 4 square feet per person, or less.
Average Flow Volume: Variable to 17 PFM.

At stairway level-of-service F, representing a space approximately 1 to 2 tread lengths long and 2 feet wide, there is a complete breakdown in traffic flow, with many stoppages. Forward progress would depend on movement of those in front. This level of service is not recommended for design.

LEVEL OF SERVICE ILLUSTRATIONS FOR STAIRWAYS

Level
of
Service

D

E

F

LEVEL OF SERVICE STANDARDS FOR STAIRWAYS
Volume (P) vs. Module (M)

Figure 4.2

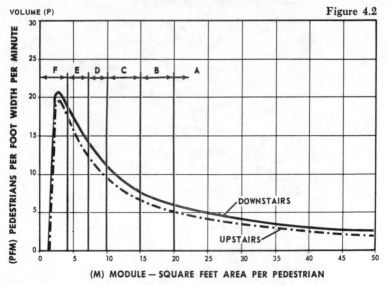

VOLUME (P)

(PFM) PEDESTRIANS PER FOOT WIDTH PER MINUTE

F E D C B A

DOWNSTAIRS

UPSTAIRS

(M) MODULE — SQUARE FEET AREA PER PEDESTRIAN

Queuing Standards

Queuing level-of-service standards are based on the human body dimensions and personal space preferences discussed in Chapter Two, and the synthesis of pedestrian mobility contained in Chapter Three. The designer should not only apply queuing standards in areas designed primarily for pedestrian waiting, such as elevator and theater lobbies, but in other areas in which queuing is likely to result from service stoppages or inadequate capacity of pedestrian service facilities. Pedestrian holding areas on the approaches to stairs, or other critical sections, should also be adequately designed to hold waiting pedestrians. Areas such as railway and bus platforms have critical pedestrian holding capacities, which, if exceeded, can cause persons to be injured by being pushed onto tracks or roadways. In addition to their ability to hold standees, queuing areas have different internal circulation requirements, based on their type of use. For example, an airport baggage claim area must be capable of holding persons waiting for baggage, as well as those moving out of the area with baggage.

Photographic illustrations and descriptions of queuing levels-of-service are shown on the following pages.

LEVEL OF SERVICE DESCRIPTIONS FOR QUEUING

Level of Service A
FREE CIRCULATION ZONE

Average Pedestrian Area Occupancy: 13 square feet per person, or more.
Average Inter-person spacing: 4 feet, or more.

At queuing level-of-service A, space is provided for standing and free circulation through the queuing area without disturbing others. Applications would include better-designed passenger concourse areas, and baggage claim areas.

Level of Service B
RESTRICTED CIRCULATION ZONE

Average Pedestrian Area Occupancy: 10-13 square feet per person.
Average Inter-person spacing: 3½-4 feet.

At queuing level-of-service B, space is provided for standing and restricted circulation through the queue without disturbing others. Applications would include railroad platforms, and passenger concourse areas.

PEDESTRIAN QUEUE IN THE A TO B RANGE

Level of Service C
PERSONAL COMFORT ZONE

Average Pedestrian Area Occupancy: 7-10 square feet per person.
Average Inter-person spacing: 3-3½ feet.

At queuing level-of-service C, space is provided for standing and restricted circulation through the queuing area by disturbing others. It is within the range of the personal comfort body buffer zone established by psychological experiments. Applications would include ordered-queue ticket-selling areas, and elevator lobbies.

Level of Service D
NO-TOUCH ZONE

Average Pedestrian Area Occupancy: 3-7 square feet per person.
Average Inter-person spacing: 2-3 feet.

At queuing level-of-service D, space is provided for standing without personal contact with others, but circulation through the queuing area is severely restricted, and forward movement is only possible as a group. Applications would include motorstair queuing areas, pedestrian safety islands, or holding areas at crosswalks. Based on psychological experiments, this level of area occupancy is not recommended for long-term periods of waiting.

PEDESTRIAN QUEUE IN THE C TO D RANGE

Level of Service E

TOUCH ZONE

Average Pedestrian Area Occupancy: 2-3 square feet per person.
Average Inter-person spacing: 2 feet or less.

At queuing level-of-service E, space is provided for standing, but personal contact with others is unavoidable. Circulation within the queuing area is not possible. This level of area occupancy can only be sustained for short periods of time without physical and psychological discomfort. The only recommended application would be for elevator occupancy.

Level of Service F

THE BODY ELLIPSE

Average Pedestrian Area Occupancy: 2 square feet per person, or less.
Average Inter-person spacing: Close contact with surrounding persons.

At queuing level-of-service F, space is approximately equivalent to the area of the human body. Standing is possible, but close unavoidable contact with surrounding standees causes physical and psychological discomfort. No movement is possible, and in large crowds the potential for panic exists.

PEDESTRIAN QUEUE IN THE F RANGE

87

Chapter Five

PEDESTRIAN MOVERS—"PEDMOVERS"

This chapter has been titled "Pedestrian Movers" to differentiate mechanical systems, designed to carry persons on foot, from the many new forms of "people movers" that employ vehicles. The chapter's main focus is on elevators, motorstairs and moving walks, with a brief discussion of "people-mover" systems at the end of the chapter. The mechanical principles of moving people and goods on elevators have been in use for thousands of years. Efficient, safe elevator transportation has made possible the concentrated, multi-story development of our modern urban centers. Escalators are a comparatively recent innovation in this long history, but wide public acceptance of escalators has made their use almost mandatory for many low-rise applications. Moving walks have been used to shorten walking distances, but they may be advantageously substituted for escalators in certain circumstances.

There is a traffic-flow distinction between the use of elevators, which provide on-demand service, and escalators and moving walks, which constantly offer service which may, or may not, be constantly utilized. The practical capacity of these constant-service devices has created problems for some designers, because of an incomplete understanding of traffic and human characteristics of their use. Similar misconceptions have led to overstated claims of capacity for some recently proposed people-mover systems.

Elevators

The elevator is the most universally accepted mechanical pedestrian mover. Elevators represent one of the earliest forms of mechanical aids for the movement of people and goods. Undoubtedly, the Egyptians devised various types of elevator systems to move the massive stone blocks of the pyramids. Archimedes is credited with building the first elevator, using large wheels for its mechanical advantage, in 236 B.C. Shaftways designed to accommodate guided elevator platforms have been discovered in Roman ruins. The palace of the Emperor Nero reportedly contained three elevators. Elevators were used to lift animals to the arena level of the ancient Roman Coliseum. The

French fortress of Mont St. Michel contains an example of an elevator hoist dating from the eleventh century. All of these early lifting devices had serious safety deficiencies, because the hoisting rope was made of fiber, which often broke without warning. Modern elevators date from 1853, when Elisha Otis invented the first safety device designed to prevent the lift platform from falling freely due to a broken hoisting rope. The technical advance of elevators was aided further by the development of more reliable steel-cable rope, and the steam engine. Safe, efficient, elevator systems have made the dense, high-rise development of our modern cities possible. Recent technical innovations in elevator engineering include shaft speeds as high as 1600 to 1800 feet per minute, automatic operation to meet variations in traffic demand, and the double-deck elevator.

The traffic design of elevator systems has been developed to a rather exact science, using techniques of analysis based on the operating characteristics of the elevator, boarding characteristics of the users, and user traffic patterns. Elevator operating characteristics would include lobby configurations, cab configurations and their practical standing capacity, shaft acceleration and deceleration speeds, and door opening and closing speeds. The standing capacity of an elevator is based on the assumption of an average area occupancy of about 2 square feet per person. Elevators may be crowded to area occupancies of as low as 1.5 square feet per person, but this is undesirable, and unlikely under most normal conditions. Rules of human conduct vary in elevators, affecting their standing capacity. If traffic is composed of groups of persons known to each other, lower per-person area occupancies are tolerated. In more formal situations, as in a hotel elevator, close crowding of elevator occupants is not readily accepted. As discussed in Chapter Three, unavoidable contact between standing pedestrians is likely to occur at area occupancies below 2¾ square feet per person. Heavier winter clothing, and the presence of baggage of packages, increases the area needed for the avoidance of contact. Most persons require 3 square feet or more to feel comfortable in an elevator.

The key element of a well-designed elevator system is an understanding of the traffic demand patterns of the users. A high-rise building will naturally have peaks that are tied to the work schedules of its employees. Office workers generally will have different working hours than industrial workers and maintenance staff. The presence or absence of in-house eating facilities will

The Port of New York Authority World Trade Center.

WORLD TRADE CENTER SKY-LOBBY ELEVATOR SYSTEM

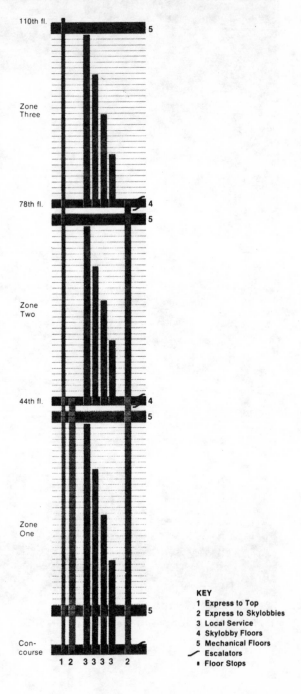

Figure 5.1

affect the severity of the lunch peak. Staggering of work schedules can produce a more balanced use of elevator facilities, and higher levels-of-service. The quality of service of an elevator system is usually based on average waiting time. The tolerance level for an acceptable waiting time for elevator service has been established at about 30 seconds for commercial buildings, and 60 seconds for residential buildings.

Computer simulation is being used increasingly to determine the passenger service levels of larger systems. Simulation inputs include building traffic patterns, and elevator shaft speeds, door opening speeds, and dwell times. The dwell time is the time taken to load and unload the elevator. Dwell times are one of the more complex simulation inputs, because they are a function of the number of persons in the elevator, as well as the number getting on and off. Dwell times are very often the most time-consuming element of elevator use and, are therefore, a significant determinant of capacity. The computer simulation technique has been used to evaluate elevator passenger service levels for the world's tallest building complex, the 9-million-square-foot World Trade Center in New York City. Each of the two 110-story tower buildings has 104 local and express elevators, to accommodate the Center's 50,000 employees and estimated 80,000 daily visitors.

Large buildings require optimization of elevator service because elevator shafts reduce net usable (and rentable) floor area. In very tall buildings, such as the John Hancock building in Chicago, the World Trade Center in New York, and Sears Tower in Chicago, conventional single-shaft elevator systems would consume considerable amounts of usable building space on lower floors. Space savings were realized in these projects by using "sky lobby" concepts, which, in effect, divide the building into two or three buildings stacked one upon the other. Passengers destined for the upper floors of the building take high-speed elevators to an intermediate sky lobby, where they transfer to upper-floor elevators. Vertical shafts for upper and lower segments of the building are used in common, by two to three elevators stacked above each other. (See Figure 5.1). The sky lobby system at the Trade Center resulted in an estimated 13 per cent increase in gross rentable floor area, over conventional elevator arrangements.

The accepted innovation for increasing elevator capacity is the double-deck elevator. The system is installed in the Time-Life Building in Chicago, and the John Hancock Tower in Boston and as shuttle elevators to the Skylobbies in the Sears Tower. Double-deck elevators are two stories high, with upper and lower compartments. Passengers enter these elevators from two entrance lobbies, a lower lobby serving odd floors, and an upper lobby serving even floors. (See Figures 5.2 and 5.3). This has the advantage of reducing pedestrian traffic concentrations in entrance lobby areas. Double-deck elevators operate in the conventional way in response to passenger calls in both compartments. In peaks, when this system is most efficient, stops would be made in response to calls in both upper and lower compartments. At other times, persons in one compartment might be required to wait momentarily while a call is answered in the other, or the one compartment can be re-programmed to serve all floors. Under typical conditions, double-decking is estimated to increase elevator capacity by one hundred per cent, reducing the required number of elevator shafts in half. Double-deck elevators can also be combined with the sky lobby concept, to produce even greater space savings (See Figure 5.3).

Figure 5.2

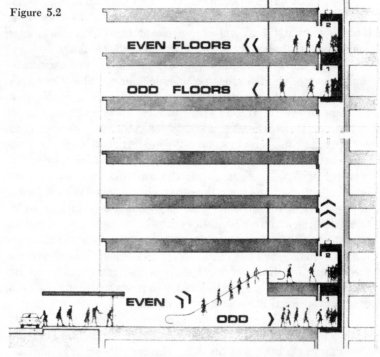

DOUBLE DECK ELEVATORS — LOBBY CONFIGURATION

94

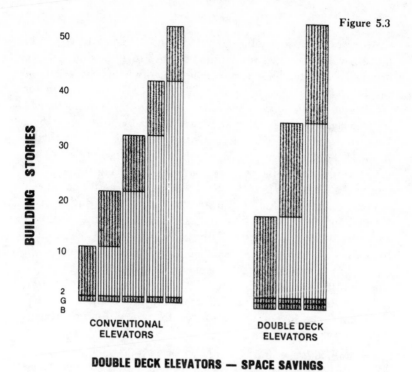

DOUBLE DECK ELEVATORS — SPACE SAVINGS

Figure 5.3

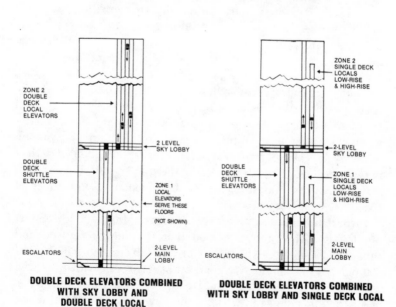

DOUBLE DECK ELEVATORS COMBINED WITH SKY LOBBY AND DOUBLE DECK LOCAL

DOUBLE DECK ELEVATORS COMBINED WITH SKY LOBBY AND SINGLE DECK LOCAL

Escalators

An escalator is a combined vertical and horizontal pedestrian mover, which provides a continuous series of individual pallets, or treads, for standing pedestrians. The origin of the escalator can be traced to 1859, when Nathan Ames obtained a patent for "Revolving Stairs", a device consisting of steps linked together to form a continuous, moving stairway driven by rollers. In 1892, Jesse Reno patented a device called an "Endless Conveyor", described as a sliding mechanical incline. The "steps" of this conveyor were actually flat, grooved sections, following the angle of incline. In 1900, the first practical moving stair based on Reno's patent was installed in the 59th street station of the Third Avenue Manhattan elevated line. This first unit had a rise of 24 feet, was 18 inches wide, and inclined about 25 degrees. In this same year, the Otis Elevator Company installed a similar escalator, based on an 1899 patent by Charles D. Seeberger, at the Paris Exhibition. About 1910, the Otis Elevator Company acquired the patent rights of Reno, Seeberger and another inventor named Wheeler, combining each inventor's best design features into a unit resembling today's installations.

The normal angle of incline of escalators is 30 degrees. Operating speeds in the United States are usually either 90 or 120 feet per minute, measured along the incline. This is within the range of the average stair-climbing speeds reported in Chapter Three. Some escalators incorporate dual-speed features, so that they can be run at both speeds, with the higher speed being used during periods of peak demand. Operating speeds, angles, and widths, of both escalators and moving walks, are established by the American Standard Safety Code for elevators. The angle and speed of escalators are more variable in Europe. An escalator angle of 35 degrees is used for units at the Montparnasse Station of the Paris Metro transit system. A speed of about 180 feet per minute has been reported in the Leningrad, Russia, subway system. Several studies have been made of the effect of speed on escalator capacity, including a study by the London Transport system of escalator speeds varying from 100 to 185 feet per minute. This study revealed that the optimum speed and capacity of a 48-inch-wide escalator was 145 feet per minute, and 150 persons per minute. Comparison of this result with American use is difficult, because of the well-established English practice of standees keeping to the right, to allow moving pedestrians to pass on the left. Signs adjacent to escalators also state this rule.

It is interesting to note that the practice of walking on a moving escalator probably produces little if any gain in escalator capacity, because the moving pedestrian must occupy two steps at a time during stair locomotion, cancelling out much of the capacity advantage that may be gained through the faster combined speed. The practice has the advantage of shortening pedestrian trip times for those who choose to walk. This is important in deep subway systems, with long, high-rise escalators, as in London. A study of dual-speed escalators in this country found that a one-third increase in the speed of the unit, from 90 to 120 feet per minute, resulted in approximately a 12 per cent increase in pedestrian use, under the constant pressure of heavy traffic volumes and frequent queuing.

Escalator manufacturers rate the theoretical capacity of their units on the basis of speed, assumed occupancy per step, and 100 per cent step utilization. Numerous observations have shown that 100 per cent step utilization is never obtained, even with the heaviest traffic pressure and use by the most knowledgeable and agile pedestrians, including commuters. For this reason, a

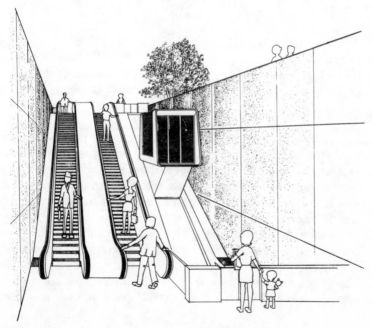

Proposed inclined elevator for the handicapped, using the same space as a conventional escalator.

nominal, or practical, design capacity is often suggested for escalator design. The manufacturer's theoretical capacity is based on 5 persons for each 4 steps on a 32 inch-wide escalator, and 2 persons per step for a 48 inch-wide escalator. The nominal capacities are observed averages reported by Strakosch in the book: *Vertical Transportation - Elevators and Escalators*, John Wiley Publishers, 1983 edition. Actual capacity is considerably lower as shown below and is generally one person every other step on a 32 inch-wide escalator and one person per step on a 48 inch-wide escalator. NOTE: Recent changes in designations now refer to step width rather than hip width, 48″ therefore is now 40″ (1000 mm) and 32″ is now 24″ (600 mm).

Table 5-A

THEORETICAL AND NOMINAL ESCALATOR CAPACITIES

Width At Hip (Inches)	Width At Tread (Inches)		Maximum Theoretical Capacity Persons/Hour	Nominal Capacity Persons/ Hour	Nominal Capacity Persons/ Minute
32	24	(1)	5,000	2,040	34
		(2)	6,700	2,700	45
48	40	(1)	8,000	4,080	68
		(2)	10,700	5,400	90

(1) incline speed 90 feet per minute, 68 steps per minute.
(2) incline speed 120 feet per minute, 89 steps per minute.

Although these nominal capacity ratings provide a useful guideline for comparing escalator sizes and speeds, they do not explain the phenomenon of empty steps that are often seen when escalators are under heavy use, nor the wide variations in capacity that have been reported by various agencies. Escalator capacities should be determined on the same rational basis that is followed in elevator capacity analysis. The real determinants of this use are the arrival process, and boarding characteristics, of the users. An intermittent arrival process, such as that described in Chapter Three, can result in gaps during which escalator steps go by unused. In addition, a transit arrival pattern with scheduled

ILLUSTRATION OF VACANT STEPS
ON HEAVY TRAFFIC ESCALATOR

spacing between trains can produce gaps of unused escalator capacity. Unused escalator steps can also be caused by the user's inability to board the unit quickly enough, or be a simple personal desire for a more comfortable human space.

A comparison of the standing areas provided for pedestrians on escalator treads illustrates the potential for personal space interaction. The 32-inch escalator (hip width), has a 15-inch projected tread length and a 24-inch tread width, which provides an average standing area of 2.7 square feet per pedestrian, at the manufacturer's assumed ocupancy of 1¼ persons per step. The 48-inch escalator, with a 40-inch tread width, allows only 2.1 square feet standing area per person at the manufacturer's theoretical assumption of double step occupancy. These standing areas are within the zone of unavoidable contact between pedestrians, established in Chapter Three. At the observed nominal capacities, standing areas are above 4 square feet per pedestrian, which is greater than the "touch zone" noted in studies of elevator loading and occupancy. Personal area preference, therefore, provides a partial explanation of the phenomenon of vacant steps on escalators in heavy traffic. When boarding an escalator, a person has the option of choosing a step position directly behind and beside another person, with the risk of brushing against him or her, or letting that step go by, thus obtaining a more comfortable personal space. This prospect of leaving a gap would depend on the individual's own buffer zone image, the physical size of adjacent persons, or the presence of baggage or packages. Tending to confirm this premise, average peak volume use of escalators at one large transportation terminal has been observed to be slightly lower in winter, which has been attributed to bulkier clothing.

A slow-motion picture study of persons boarding escalators offers a further insight into the vacant-step phenomenon. Pedestrians were photographed as they passed through the entrance section of the escalator, comprised of the comb plate length and first tread length, which were readily identifiable in photographs. (See illustration). An editing device was used to determine boarding times, by counting the number of photographic frames required for a pedestrian to pass through the entrance section, and translating the number of frames into an equivalent boarding time. The accuracy of the technique was confirmed by counts of peak volumes obtained while the escalator was under constant queuing pressure.

MOTORSTAIR BOARDING SEQUENCE

SLOW MOTION PHOTOGRAPHY – 24 FRAMES PER SECOND

WOMEN
APPROACHING
MOTORSTAIR

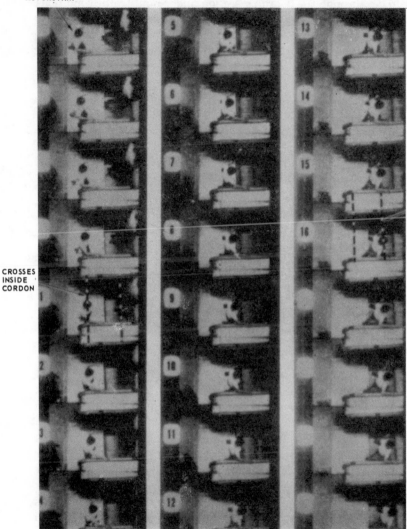

CROSSES
INSIDE
CORDON

CROSSE
OUTSID
CORDON

BOARDING TIME = $\frac{16 \text{ FRAMES}}{24 \text{ FRAMES}} \times 1 \text{ SEC} = .67 \text{ SECONDS}$

At a normal walking speed of 4.5 feet per second, pedestrians could be expected to pass through the entrance section in less than six-tenths of a second. Very few pedestrians were capable of this performance, with the average pedestrian taking about one second to get through the boarding section under light traffic conditions. Females were found to take longer than males, and both heavy traffic and baggage produced measurable increases in boarding times. Table 5-B is a summary of the boarding times observed for the 48-inch escalator.

Table 5-B

PHOTOGRAPHIC SURVEY-
ESCALATOR BOARDING TIMES

(Average Time in Seconds)

| | Light Traffic | | Heavy Traffic |
	(No Baggage)	(With Baggage)	(No Baggage)
MEN	0.95	1.01	1.16
WOMEN	1.06	1.08	1.18
COMBINED	0.98	1.05	1.17

The average headway of 1.17 seconds, observed under constant heavy-traffic conditions, is equivalent to a escalator use of 103 pedestrians per minute, approximately equal to the observed nominal capacity.

The study showed some other interesting results. Figure 5.4 shows frequency distributions of pedestrian boarding times under light traffic conditions, with and without baggage, and under heavy traffic, with baggage. Baggage was also found to cause slight, but measurable, increases in heavy traffic boarding times. If a line is drawn on these distributions equivalent to the common 90- and 120-foot-per-minute speeds of escalators, it can be seen that the normal boarding times of some pedestrians are not fast enough for boarding the first escalator step at the higher speed. This accounts for the observed lower percentage of tread occupancies

BOARDING TIMES — 48 INCH ESCALATORS

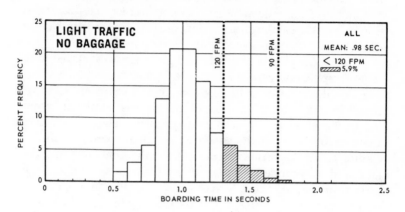

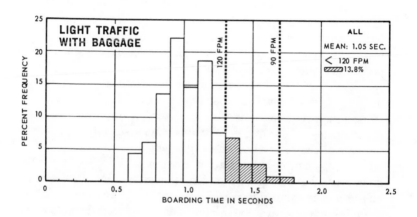

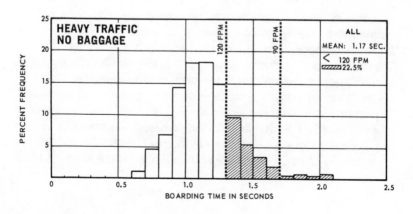

on the faster units. The photographic study indicates that the nominal capacity is a reasonable estimate of use under constant demand, but the reductions in this nominal capacity can be expected if traffic is intermittent, composed of persons with baggage or packages, and if the escalator speed is increased.

The pedestrian boarding time distributions developed in the photographic study were put to use in another way. They were introduced into a General Purpose Simulation System (GPSS/360) computer program and escalator utilization was simulated for varying traffic demands. The computer program selected pedestrian inter-arrival times at the escalator, assigned boarding times according to the proportion of male and female users and traffic density, and determined average utilization, queue lengths, and pedestrian waiting times. The computer simulation program produced an accurate picture of observed queuing lengths and waiting times that are known to occur, typically, at this escalator. The significance of this computer simulation technique is in its versatility, which affords the designer a means of evaluating the impact of specific traffic patterns and user characteristics on escalator utilization, producing reasonable predictions of actual escalator use, pedestrian queue size, and waiting times.

The possibility that escalators can generate large queues, even at traffic levels below the capacity of the unit, is often overlooked by designers. On the basis of probabilities, a surge in flow and a group of slower-boarding pedestrians can reasonably be expected to occur at the same time, causing a long, but temporary, queue, which can cause crowding or disrupt other nearby traffic movements. For example, in the computer simulation run described above, a maximum queue of 98 persons occurred at one point, even though the average arrival rate was slightly below the nominal capacity of the unit. On the basis of an average area of 5 square feet per person area occupancy observed for escalator queues, a 500-square-foot clear area would be required at the escalator approaches to accommodate this surge of queuing pedestrians. If the nominal capacity of the escalator is exceeded, much larger backup spaces are needed. The discharge end of an escalator also must provide sufficient space to accommodate pedestrians being *mechanically* fed off the escalator, and to avoid conflicts with other traffic streams. Mechanically is emphasized because an escalator discharges pedestrians into an area regardless of whether the area has sufficient space to accept them or not. If the space at the outlet end happens to be a railroad platform, the potential exists for persons to be pushed off the platform by the continuously delivered pedestrians coming off the escalator. In these situations, controls must be established to avoid crowding the escalator outlet area beyond its capacity to accommodate queuing pedestrians.

The impact of escalator stoppages for maintenance and repair should also be given consideration in design. Adequate supplementary stationary stairs should be situated close to the escalator. Provisions should also be made for performing routine preventive maintenance without stopping the escalator. Where possible, the New York City Transit Authority locates machine rooms inside the upper supporting truss of its escalators, so that a maintenance man can lubricate and inspect the unit without interrupting its operation.

Escalator landing areas must be carefully designed to avoid traffic conflicts and to provide sufficient area for queuing pedestrians.

Moving Walks

A moving walk is a conveyance that provides a flat, continuous, moving surface, of pallets or a rubber belt, on which the pedestrian may stand or walk. Moving walks are installed on level surfaces, to shorten walking distances, or on inclines of up to 12 degrees, to provide both horizontal and vertical movement. The earliest escalators resembled the moving walk, because the individual treads were not stepped, but followed the incline of the escalator. Moving sidewalks were advocated as early as 1874, when there was a proposal for an elevated moving sidewalk and people-mover system in Manhattan. The proposed loop system was to be comprised of a continuous, moving sidewalk, running parallel to a faster conveyor carrying passenger cars. In 1893, a system of this type was installed at the Chicago Columbian Exposition. Thé system, which carried 2.7 million passengers, was comprised of a boarding stage of a continuous series of pallets moving at 3 miles per hour, and a second stage of a continuous series of cars with seats moving at 6 miles per hour. Similar systems were installed at the Berlin Exposition of 1896, and the Paris Exposition of 1900. The Paris installation carried 8 million passengers. These innovative systems captured the imagination of the public at that time in much the same way that monorail has today.

In the early 1900's formal recommendations were made to the New York State Public Service Commission for combined moving-walk and people-mover systems for the Brooklyn and Williamsburg bridges in Manhattan. A subway line was also proposed between 10th and 42nd streets. This line was to have the more ambitious seated-stage speed of 12 miles per hour, reached in progressive moving-walk stages of 3, 6 and 9 miles per hour. The Continuous Transit Corporation, advocates of the moving-walk and people-mover subway, estimated that the system would provide a seated capacity far in excess of any conventional rail subway. In 1909, the New York City Board of Estimate authorized a formal study of such a system under 34th Street, extending from Second to Ninth Avenues. In the 1920's, the Continuous Transit Corporation again proposed a shuttle system under 42nd Street, between Grand Central Terminal and Times Square, with the seated-stage speed of 9 miles per hour. At that time, a large-scale experimental model was built in Jersey City, New Jersey. The system was said to have a seated capacity of 35,640 persons per hour, compared to the 4,400 seats and 17,600 passengers provided by the then existing Times Square shuttle operation. Little information is available to explain why these systems were never built. However, one disadvantage of large-scale, continuous moving systems is their "weak-link" vulnerability. When a system is comprised of a passive roadbed and multiple, individually powered units, such as with conventional transit, disabled units can easily be removed from the system for repair. With larger, continuous moving systems, the entire system must be shut down for repair. The loss of service due to system down-times can be lessened by installation of parallel systems, and by designing for system redundancy and preventive maintenance efficiency. Preventive maintenance efficiency, or maintainability, is enhanced in the initial design by assuring convenient maintenance access, and machine design that allows for quick replacement of working parts, particularly those parts that are subject to greater probabilities of failure. It would also include provision for storage of a supply of replacement parts close to the system.

There are two basic categories of moving walks, the **pallet** type, a continuous system of flat, grooved treads, using virtually the same machinery parts as an escalator, and the **belt** type, a continuous, conveyor-like, grooved rubber belt, supported by rollers. The steel pallet systems are not as common as the continuous belt. The Bank Station of the London Underground transit system has two, heavily used, 48-inch-wide, 300-foot-long, 42-foot-rise, steel-treaded pallet type units, capable of speeds of up to 180 feet per minute. The capacity of each of these units has been rated by London Transport at 10,000 passengers per hour. There are numerous examples of the belt-type system. One of the longest and most notable is at the Montparnasse Station of the Paris Metro. This installation is comprised of three, 44-inch-wide, 607-foot-long units, running at speeds of 164 feet per minute. Two of the units operate in the direction of peak flow. The Paris Metro also has two 430-foot-long units in operation at the Chatelet Station. The riding characteristics of the pallet and belt types are similar, except that the undulations of the supporting rollers on the belt type are usually sensed through the feet of the pedestrian. This presents no serious problem if belt tension is maintained at a satisfactory level.

Moving belts are generally run at faster speeds than escalators, but slower speeds are often used for installations that are patronized by larger percentages of slower-reacting shoppers and older persons. Where pedestrians are likely to be distracted, such as in amusement areas, slower speeds have also been found to be more desirable. Level moving walks can easily be used by persons with shopping carts or baby carriages, and by handicapped persons in wheelchairs. However, these uses are limited on sloped units. Some shopping centers have provided special shopping carts with wheels that intermesh with the grooves of the rubber belt, to facilitate their use on sloped units.

The capacity of moving walks is rated in much the same way as escalators, by an assumed pedestrian occupancy, and the operating speed of the unit. The rated capacities supplied by one manufacturer are shown in Table 5-C.

Table 5-C

MOVING WALK CAPACITY
Speed: 120 feet per minute

Item	Single Lane	Double Lane
Hip Width (Inches)	30	42
Belt Width (Inches)	24	36
Theoretical Capacity		
Persons per hour	4800	9600
Persons per minute	80	160 ←
Nominal Capacity		
Persons per minute	40	80

The theoretical capacity of these units is based on a spacing of 2 feet between pedestrians and single occupancy on the 24-inch unit, and double occupancy on the 42-inch unit. The maximum observed use of a 44-inch wide walkway is 100 persons per minute after a performance at the Holly-wood Bowl, California. The double-width unit has the deficiency that it does not allow sufficient shoulder width for two persons to stand abreast, or to pass each other comfortably. Observations of the use of a unit of this type confirmed that on occasion, a single, standing pedestrian, particularly one with baggage, would stop or hinder by-passing pedestrians. The lack of

ABOVE N NARROW + YET RATE

Moving walks are adaptable for use by the handicapped.

A cut-away view of a moving walk illustrating the drive unit, belt support rollers and comb plate.

sufficient shoulder width was also observed to cause difficulties at the entrance of the unit when two persons approached it simultaneously. A slow-motion photography study of boarding times showed slightly slower average boarding times for a double-width moving belt, as compared to a 48-inch escalator. The escalator provides 4 inches more width at the tread.

The capacity of moving walks is based on the assumption of standing pedestrians. It has often been stated that when pedestrians walk on a moving belt the capacity of the unit is increased, even doubled. This is not correct. As discussed previously, the average pedestrian requires an area of about 25 square feet for a near-normal walking speed of 250 feet per minute, about twice the speed of the belt. Although the pedestrian's relative speed when walking on a belt is about three times the belt speed, the pedestrian actually requires more than three times the area for walking than the manufacturer's capacity assumption. This actually results in a slight decrease in capacity if all pedestrians walk on a moving belt. However, the practice of walking on moving belts is to be encouraged, because of the pedestrian's own time savings.

There is a significant amount of research currently underway on the development of variable-speed moving walks. These units would be boarded at conventional 90- or 120-foot-per-minute speeds, and then would accelerate the standing pedestrian to speeds of up to 10 miles per hour. The philosophy behind the development of these systems is that there is a speed gap between walking speed (3 MPH) and the speed of most rapid transit systems (15 MPH+). This speed gap becomes more significant for trips within airports or central business districts, where rapid transit cannot satisfactorily satisfy internal trip demands. The Battelle Institute of Geneva is investigating the feasibility of the Integrator, a continuous feeder system used as a boarding stage for a "Speedaway" transporter belt, travelling at 10 miles per hour. Pedestrians would board the Integrator in a direction transverse to the Speedaway transporter, and then be angularly accelerated by the Integrator until it is running parallel and at the same speed as the transporter. Pedestrians would then board the 10 MPH transporter. Researchers at Johns Hopkins University's Applied Physics Laboratory are working on a linear accelerator with much the same configuration as a pallet-type moving walk, but capable of accelerating from 1.7 MPH to 5 MPH through changing tread geometry. All these systems are being designed with attention to human acceleration and deceleration tolerances.

People Movers

"People Movers" is a rather broad, generic term which could encompass any type of vehicle or mechanical movement system used by man. This discussion is limited to some of the smaller systems, which might be typically used by pedestrians for internal transportation within an airport or central business district. The basic prerequisites of such systems are that they have ready access for boarding and discharge, and that acceleration and deceleration be accomplished within short distances. The systems may be classified either as **passive** vehicle types, in which propulsion is provided by the roadbed, or **tractive** vehicle types, in which the roadbed is passive but may supply power and guidance to the vehicle. The Carveyor and the Disneyland People Mover are examples of the first category, and Starrcar is an example of the latter.

The Carveyor is a continuous service system, employing a passenger car with facing seats placed on a moving belt. At stations and terminals the passenger car is decelerated to 1.5 MPH, and passengers board the car by means of a parallel moving walk running at this speed. After passengers board the car, it is accelerated to 15 MPH, by a series of rollers. The Disneyland People Mover, which has been in active use for some years, resembles the Carveyor with the exception that instead of the car being accelerated onto a moving belt, car traction is supplied by a continuous series of rotating rollers, placed in the roadbed. Operating difficulties are sometimes experienced in wet weather, due to loss of traction on the rollers. The people-mover makes use of attendants at its terminal ends to assist persons on and off cars.

The Starrcar would be typical of systems in which individual vehicles are provided with guidance and power from the roadway, and operate under computer control. Starrcar can also be designed to operate over conventional roadway systems, with entrance into the guideway system at selected points. The Starrcar could also operate in a closed system, providing on-demand service similar to an elevator. The advantages of individual powered vehicles is that in the event of a vehicle malfunction, they can be taken off the line. This lessens the probability of a system-wide breakdown.

It is perhaps worth repeating that the true capacity of continuous moving systems is not a function of the number of seats or total standing area provided. Arrival characteristics and human capabilities will determine the practical or working capacity of these systems. If a person hesitates, or finds difficulty in boarding such a system, then unused capacity will pass by. There are many persons who balk at using mechanical systems, or who, under some circumstances, may refuse to use them altogether. Conditions that exist at amusement areas or expositions do not necessarily represent a true picture of a system in daily use by the general population. Attendants are very often provided at these places to encourage and assist the balking pedestrian. In addition, many handicapped persons avoid these places because of expected difficulties. In developing the capacity of such systems, it is recommended that the boarding characteristics of a true sample of the user population be closely examined. The only satisfactory way of collecting such data in a meaningful manner is through slow-motion moving picture analysis. Each movement may be accurately timed and evaluated, and, if necessary, the films can be run over and over again, until the human processes are clearly understood. These user boarding characteristics, combined with the expected traffic patterns and demand characteristics of the particular application, are the only true determinants of capacity and actual use.

Starrcar is an example of a tractive-vehicle, passive-roadbed people-mover system.

Carveyor is an example of a passive-vehicle, tractive-roadbed people-mover system.

Chapter Six

ELEMENTS OF PEDESTRIAN PLANNING

The pedestrian planning process follows the classic sequence of problem definition, identification of restraints, determination of program objectives, establishment of study scope and procedures, collection and analysis of data, development of alternative solutions, final design, and program implementation. A planning program for pedestrians may involve one building, a small group of buildings, a downtown core network, or even larger systems of interlocking networks. Project scope may range from a basic low-budget improvement program, gradually implemented over a long time period, to a large capital project with accelerated priorities. This chapter deals with the general objectives of pedestrian improvement programs, study procedures and techniques, and some methods of plan implementation. The discussion generally follows the schematic illustration shown in Figure 6.1.

Planning Goals and Objectives

The primary goals and objectives of an improvement program for pedestrians are: safety, security, convenience, continuity, comfort, system coherence and attractiveness. All goals are interrelated and overlapping. Improvements in one objective generally result in opportunities for improvements in the others. The basic concern of **pedestrian safety** is the reduction of the pedestrian-vehicle conflict. The two fundamental means of attaining this objective are: by space separation, either horizontal or vertical, or by time separation. Traffic signalization represents an example of separation of pedestrians and vehicles in time, but with most conventional signalization methods the pedestrian is still exposed to conflicts with turning vehicles. There have been attempts to reduce or eliminate these conflicts by using an advanced, or delayed, green indication for turning vehicles, allowing them to turn outside the pedestrian walk cycle. An exclusive pedestrian signal phase, called the "all-walk," or "scramble" system, is used at busy downtown intersections in some cities. During this signal phase, pedestrians are given exclusive crossing rights, and may even cross diagonally within the intersection. Time separation of vehicles and pedestrians by traffic signalization has the disadvantage of inducing greater concentrations of pedestrians at corners and on sidewalks. Corner concentrations are caused by accumulations of pedestrians waiting to cross the streets. Sidewalk concentrations are induced by the alternating imposition of the signal cycle on pedestrian flow, causing denser flow platoons than would occur with a normal free-flow pattern, unrestrained by signal interruptions.

Imperial Rome's restrictions against heavy vehicular traffic in the central city during daylight hours represent another form of time separation. A more recent example is the closing of streets in New York's crowded financial district during lunch hours, to facilitate the movement of extremely dense pedestrian traffic. Other New York streets have been temporarily closed for recreational, sightseeing and shopping purposes during weekends. New York has also instituted a staggered work hours program, a time separation plan with broad implications. The program has reduced pedestrian congestion in buildings, streets and in transit stations and trains. This program hopes to balance the distribution of employee work schedules to reduce peaking effects.

The City of New York has closed streets in the crowded downtown financial district to facilitate pedestrian movement.

THE PEDESTRIAN PLANNING PROCESS

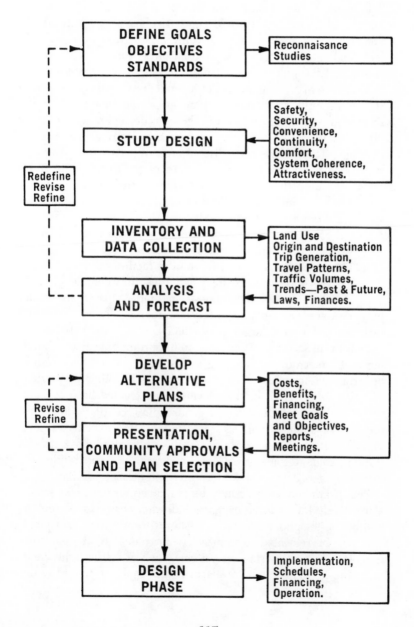

Figure 6.1

117

The horizontal or vertical separation of pedestrians and vehicles is a means of satisfying almost all pedestrian improvement objectives. Horizontal separation can be accomplished by establishment of a pedestrian precinct, or mall, where vehicular intrusion is restricted or eliminated. This concept has been used in the development of many suburban shopping centers, and is also a feature of many new town designs. Exclusive pedestrian malls are also being created in some central city areas by closing selected city streets. Vertical separation of pedestrians and vehicles is attained through the use of underpasses or overpasses.

There are many examples of independent overpass or underpass structures built at locations where an active pedestrian traffic linkage crosses a busy highway. These grade separations are very often installed in reaction to a heavy pedestrian accident experience. There have been discouraging results where these installations were located off the route of pedestrian trip desire lines, or where their use causes increased time and energy expenditures to climb stairs. Studies conducted by the Road Research Laboratory in England showed that even when the time required to use the safer underpass or overpass is **equal** to the level walking time, only 80 per cent of those observed made use of it. The proportion of use of these safer facilities dropped sharply when this time was **greater** than the equivalent level walk. This clearly indicates that pedestrian grade separations cannot be considered as isolated safety improvements, but must be incorporated into a larger pedestrian convenience network.

Pedestrian security has become an important objective in building and street design. Building and street configurations should be arranged to enhance clear observation by other pedestrians and the police. High lighting levels, unobstructed lines of sight, and avoidance of building or landscaping configurations that provide concealment will assist in attaining this objective. Television surveillance is being increasingly used in buildings, transit stations, and at some street locations, and the possibilities for locating these devices should receive attention in design.

Pedestrian convenience may be enhanced on most city streets at relatively little capital expense. Sidewalk obstructions, such as mailboxes, telephone booths, newsstands, refuse cans, and planters, may be relocated to improve pedestrian flow at practically no cost. Other more stationary items, such as traffic light standards, fire hydrants, and fire alarm boxes, could be moved under normal replacement schedules. Zoning bonus provisions can be used as a means of encouraging developers to provide improved pedestrian circulation, access to transportation facilities, and other pedestrian amenities. Traffic control systems may be modified to facilitate pedestrian, rather than vehicular, flow. Circuitous pedestrian trip linkages around large-block street configurations can be shortened by the use of midblock connectors. Municipal ordinances can control across-the-sidewalk freight operations during certain times of the day. Staggered work hours, exclusive pedestrian streets during busy hours, and other time-separation programs, can also be promoted at very little cost. Ramped curb cuts provide convenience for handicapped pedestrians in wheelchairs, persons wheeling baby carriages, and for others who have difficulties with high curbs. Tactile trails for the blind can be installed in and around buildings that are frequented by these persons.

Continuity, convenience and comfort are the primary objectives of the new grade-separated pedestrian networks being built or planned for the future. (See Chapter Eight). These networks are either above or below street level, with both having their advantages and disadvantages. Underground systems need only be about ten feet below street level, provide full weather protection, more efficient climate control, and are easily connected to subway transit stations. Disadvantages of underground systems are in their high excavation costs, possible conflicts with sub-surface utilities, and loss of visual identity with the cityscape above. Above-ground pedestrian convenience networks have the advantage of lower construction costs and greater opportunities for integration and identification with the cityscape. The primary disadvantage of above-ground networks is their greater height above street level, required to provide vehicle clearances, making these systems difficult to relate to below-ground transit. Most of the underground pedestrian systems have evolved by connecting an existing patchwork of passages built to serve below-grade transit stations. The above-ground networks are all new developments.

The importance of system continuity cannot be overemphasized. The developers of Chase Manhattan Plaza, in the downtown financial district of Manhattan, have built well-designed pedestrian-oriented building service facilities, consisting of an elevated, attractively landscaped plaza, and generous below-ground connections to the subway. This development serves, with

119

great efficiency, the two large office buildings abutting the plaza. However, the plaza is an island without linkage connections to other buildings or transit stations in the area. The complex therefore provides little contribution to the system-wide deficiencies that exist in this crowded district.

System coherence is related to the concepts of the perception of urban space outlined in Chapter Two. Coherence is a necessary element of urban space design if the full utility of the space is to be realized. A confused pedestrian searching for orientation has limited receptivity to secondary visual inputs such as aesthetics. All elements of the urban core, including street systems, transit facilities, office buildings, civic center and theater complexes, and shopping areas, should have clear visual statements that convey their direction, function and purpose. This does not limit opportunities for variety and interest, but actually enhances it. When the pedestrian is assured of his primary concern of orientation and direction, his level of receptivity to sensory gradients, such as changes in color, light, ground slope, smells, sounds and textures, is increased. The requirements of system coherence do not limit the use of small cul-de-sac areas for special interest, if their association with the parent network is clearly demonstrated by landmarks or path orientation. System coherence is also an important element of building design, particularly for transportation terminals. An incoherent passenger terminal configuration multiplies the number of directional signs, thus decreasing individual sign effectiveness. Directional signing will not satisfactorily alleviate incoherence in building design. Signs should be considered as a supplementary message to confirm the visual statements expressed by the legibility of the building design itself.

The objective of **attractiveness** encompasses not only aesthetic design, but the sense of excitement that should be created by an urban space. Landscaping, pavement color and texture, well-designed street furniture components, fountains, and plazas increase the visual variety of the cityscape. Opportunities for introducing elements of surprise, through suddenly revealed vistas and panoramic views, should not be overlooked. Special street events, such as concerts, change-of-season festivals, amateur art sales and contests, and seasonal flower exhibits, increase the interest and vitality of any urban space. Properly managed, these events can be conducted at very little cost through the auspices of local garden and art clubs, schools and merchants.

Inventory and Data Collection

The inventory phase of the planning process requires the collection of basic data about the study area, including its physical features, land use, and the characteristics of its daily pedestrian population. The potential adaptability to change is an important underlying objective of these initial land-use studies. This adaptability may be reflected in the value, condition and type of land use, or more importantly, in the interest and enthusiasm of local business and property owners. As an illustration of adaptive development, a department store might build a pedestrian connection to a transit station, to encourage market exposure to the station's pedestrian traffic. Since adaptive development of this type requires the cooperation of business interests, an active liaison with the business community should be developed in the earliest stages of all pedestrian planning programs. This liaison can provide valuable assistance with the collection of building population and employee data. It can also result in valuable support for the final implementation of the pedestrian improvement program.

Accurate classification of land use is important because of the extreme variability of pedestrian demand and design treatment. For example, retail stores have a much different traffic pattern and design rationale than do office buildings. Similarly, the design treatment of the walkways surrounding a historical site will be quite different from that of any other land use. The inventory of land use should include the location and classification of all buildings, streets, and transportation services. Building classification includes type of use, total square feet of net usable area, estimated building value, building condition, and employee and daily transient populations. Hourly transit patronage, and auto parking accumulations on streets and in garages, should also be determined for the study area. Bus transit cash-recording tapes, turnstile counts, and parking garage check stubs provide the source for much of this data.

The physical inventory of the study area includes the configuration and dimensions of each street and sidewalk. Street inventories should note all traffic regulations, signs, signal locations and their cycle lengths, and vehicular traffic volumes. The sidewalk inventory should show the location and dimensions of building and transit system entrances, bus stops, and the location of sidewalk furniture and other impedimenta that restrict sidewalk efficiency.

Ideally, all pedestrian walking trips, including their origins and destinations, trip purposes, time of day, and volumes, should be determined. In larger pedestrian networks this information is difficult, if not impossible, to obtain, so that combinations of various sampling and analytic techniques are used to develop this data. These methods include cordon counts, origin and destination surveys, pedestrian density surveys by aerial photography, and mathematical modeling.

Cordon counts of pedestrians cannot be obtained with the same facility as the classic vehicular surveys, where license plate checks, automatic vehicle-counting devices, and street parking and garage counts can be used to determine area-wide traffic volumes and characteristics. Pedestrian cordon counts generally cover smaller areas, and are usually obtained by manual field counting, or more recently, by aerial time-lapse photography. The manual field count is a simple procedure that can provide much useful data. An experienced traffic counter can record one-directional flows of up to 10,000, and two-directional flows of up to 2,000, pedestrians per hour in each direction if traffic is uniform and not severely peaked. With lighter flows under 1,000 pedestrians per hour, supplementary information, such as pedestrian age, sex, and the origin and destination of nearby trips, may be observed and recorded. During light, off-hour pedestrian traffic, observers may be stationed on the roof of a tall building, to record pedestrian activity for several buildings or streets.

Counts should be made on "typical" days, free from the distortions of weather and other seasonal effects. Unusually hot, cold, windy or rainy weather keeps people off the streets, or defers trips into the survey area. Special events, holidays, and parades should be avoided. Unusual happenings, such as accidents or fires, may affect the validity of counts, requiring their postponement. Survey personnel should be instructed to record street or sidewalk repairs, new construction, or any incidents that may temporarily divert pedestrians into, or away from, the counting section. When an area-wide survey is conducted at a series of locations on different days, it is advisable to set up a control station that is counted on each day of the survey. The control station should be located at a high-volume section that is a typical barometer of activity for the survey area. This allows for some adjustment to the station counts for weekday variations.

Manual field count procedures usually consist of stationing survey personnel at approximate mid-block locations, away from any large traffic generators. Intersection counts are not generally conducted in heavy pedestrian traffic areas, because of manpower requirements and the difficulties connected with segregating heavy corner flows by direction. Standard hand tally recorders are used for the count, with the observer tallying passing pedestrians by direction, and then recording the running totals for each time interval, usually every five or ten minutes. If significant platooning or surging of pedestrian flow is observed, due to traffic light cycles or transit arrival patterns, shorter counting intervals may be desirable to reflect this peaking. Pedestrian totals on the hand tally and data sheet are maintained on a cumulative basis, with later subtraction to obtain "splits", or time interval counts. Short-count methods may be used to reduce the number of field personnel required for a large, area-wide survey, particularly during lower volume, off-hour periods. An example of a short counting procedure would be counting 12 minutes on one side of the street, then 12 minutes on the other, with a 3 minute break to allow for movement between counting stations. The short counts are then expanded to full half-hour and hourly counts. This system is satisfactory where no extreme short peaks are likely to occur. At heavy traffic locations it is more desirable to collect more complete peak-period data.

Special entrance counts may be made at large traffic generators, such as office buildings, theaters and department stores. These generator counts may be correlated to net floor area by classification type, and used to develop a pedestrian trip-generation model. Field counting a wide, heavy-volume section is difficult for a single observer, and several strategically placed personnel may be required. In these instances chalk markings, sidewalk joints, or some other channelizing features of the survey area must be used to delineate the counting lanes assigned to the respective personnel. Columns, poles or other vertical separations have been found to be most effective for this purpose. Where possible, temporary stanchions may be erected in heavy counting sections to help delineate counting lanes. Recording heavy pedestrian volumes is much easier if pedestrians are counted mentally in groups of five persons, with one tally recorded for each five. The tally count is then expanded afterwards in the data summary.

There has been some investigation of the possibility of developing automatic pedestrian-counting devices, similar to those available for vehicular surveys. Electric eyes have been used with reasonable effectiveness where pedestrians pass through a single lane, such as a narrow doorway, but where there are multiple pedestrian traffic lanes this system is not practical. A pneumatic rubber mat, such as those used to open supermarket doors, has been suggested as a means of measuring foot contacts, but this method would only provide approximate traffic density ratings, which would require calibration into volume data. Ultrasonic and radar detection methods have also been suggested.

Time-lapse photography has been effectively used for pedestrian counting, but usually when detailed study data is required. Time-lapse photography has a number of significant advantages: it provides a permanent record that can be referred to again and again, to obtain additional data or to illustrate specific conditions to other interested parties; it allows a microscopic analysis of flow characteristics and direction, often giving insights into unsuspected traffic flow conditions; when used for street surveys, it can supply a variety of supplementary data, such as vehicle counts, pedestrian vehicle interactions, pedestrian accumulations at crosswalks, average pedestrian walking speeds at different traffic concentrations, effects of weather or other transient conditions; with a camera speed of one frame each ten seconds, an unattended camera can provide a ten-hour sample of traffic conditions; in some instances, photographic data collection can be done using fewer personnel.

Time-lapse photography requires a movie camera capable of single-frame advance, an intervalometer, the timing device that determines the frame interval, and a single-frame advance, or "analyst" type of projector. At one time, only relatively expensive 16 mm and 35 mm time-lapse cameras and projector combinations were available. The time intervalometer controlling these cameras required either standard electrical current or heavy battery packs with electrical convertors. All film had to be hand threaded into the camera, preferably in a dark room. Much less expensive, and more adaptable, Super-8 mm systems are now available. These systems use simple film-cassette loading, and allow camera reloading in a few seconds. The intervalometer feature has been miniaturized, and designed to operate off a few small batteries. Inexpensive home movie cameras with the single-frame advance feature have also been modified for time-lapse use. These modifications are based on the use of a capacitor, or a small synchronous motor, to give the time interval, with a connection to a solenoid to actuate the single-frame shutter release.

The desirable features of a time-lapse camera for traffic studies include: shutter speed fast enough to stop pedestrian action without blurring (1/30 second or faster); wide-angle lens to maximize dimensions of the study field of view; through-the-lens viewing and focusing; frame intervals of one to two frames per second for accurate pedestrian counting, and up to one frame each ten seconds for traffic surveillance; and provision for supplementary film magazine capacity for extended studies.

Field procedure for time-lapse photography surveys is dependent on the availability of vantage points high enough to provide a view of the study area. In order to conduct a complete study of a typical intersection, a vantage point of six stories or more in height may be required. It is a worthwhile practice to shoot preliminary film footage at prospective survey locations to check camera angles and site coverage. Care must be taken to establish definitive reference points within the camera's field of view, to establish the boundary dimensions and counting lines for the survey. These reference points should be of a type that will not be obscured when pedestrian traffic fills the study area. The selection of the frame interval will depend on the length of the camera's field of view, and the type and amount of detail required. For detailed studies, or dense pedestrian flow, short frame intervals of approximately two frames per second may be required. If less detailed low-volume cordon counts are sought, the frame interval would be determined by camera field length and the time the pedestrian would be in view. For example, with a 50-foot field length, a walking pedestrian would be in view for about 10 seconds, so that a pedestrian would appear on 4 to 5 photographic frames with a 2-second frame interval. The time interval of the camera should be periodically checked, using a stop watch, for possible time variations caused by battery drain. A safe practice is to replace batteries frequently, since they are inexpensive. A clock is sometimes placed within the camera's field of view to assist in time recording. An outdoor clock may be located in the study area, and this can be included in the photos.

Data take-off from time-lapse photography is quite simple, and can be done with a minimum of training. However, it is a tedious process, and frequent rest periods are advisable. Desktop projection is desirable to simplify data take-off and recording. A wall screen projection is adequate, but it requires up-and-down head movements that disrupt the data take-off. The desk projection allows the drawing of guide lines, use of overlays, and other aids to define the study area. Desk-top projection can be obtained by using a reflecting rear-projection screen or by lens arrangements. A microfilm viewer has also been used to provide satisfactory desk-top projection.

Pedestrian volume counts may be taken off projected photographs quickly by establishing a cordon line on the projected picture, and advancing the film in single-frame sequences. A hand tally is useful for the counting process. The number of pedestrians crossing the cordon, say in ten frame sequences, is recorded and translated into volumes by dividing by the time it took to take the original photography. Counting pedestrian accumulations at crosswalks is aided by projection on a control grid, the use of overlays, and a check-off system.

Sky Count is an aerial photography data collection method adapted from the aerial intelligence techniques used by the armed services. It can be used to collect, and permanently record, a considerable variety of important transportation and land-use data. For example, a single data collection flight over an airport can determine parking lot occupancy, length of checkout lines, roadway traffic volume, speed and composition, aircraft apron occupancy and other incidental data. Sky-Count techniques have been used for pedestrian studies in both midtown and downtown Manhattan. In addition to supplying data on the concentrations of pedestrians on sidewalks, the Sky Count photos included vehicular traffic density and composition. This data is useful for determining pedestrian/vehicle interactions. Sky Count data may be collected from either a helicopter or a light plane. The operating cost of the light plane is smaller, but tall buildings or other flight restrictions often curtail its use. A flight pattern is established by data requirements and the capabilities of the camera. A series of timed, sequentially overlapping photographs is taken over the study area. After processing, the photographs are highly magnified, and the instantaneous pedestrian and vehicle counts are obtained. Successive flights show changes in traffic concentrations during the survey period.

Figure 6.2 presents a contour plot of pedestrian densities obtained in a downtown Manhattan Sky-Count survey. In order to develop these contours, data cells were established at the sixty-four intersections in the survey area. The population of each of these intersections was obtained by counting pedestrians within a half-block of the intersection on each street. The population counts of each intersection were then assigned as point values to their respective data cells. Pedestrian populations were segregated in levels of fifty, and each level was plotted as contours on the survey map. The contour analysis map gives the location, duration, and magnitude of pedestrian demand in the entire study area. The Regional Plan Association of New York has used similar Sky-Count data, combined with observed pedestrian trip-generation rates, to develop a mathematical model to predict street concentrations of pedestrians, based on land use and other variables.

The Origin and Destination survey is the classic method of obtaining transportation trip data. Depending on methodology and scope, the survey can determine the socio-economic characteristics of the trip maker, his trip frequency, route and purpose. It also provides information on modal choice and the location and trip-attraction rates of traffic generating centers. Origin and destination surveys may be conducted by home interview (either in-person or telephone), by mailed questionnaires, by field distribution of questionnaires, with collection at terminal points or by postcard mailback, or by selective distribution to controlled populations, such as groups of employees at specific buildings. Home-interview methods are generally more costly, and are not commonly used.

The postcard mailback survey is the most popular form of Origin and Destination survey, because it is convenient and gives a reasonably good return if properly publicized by the news media. Dimensional control of the sampling populations and questionnaire distribution is important since the sample data will be expanded and treated as representative of the whole trip population. This requires that the total number of persons entering the study zone by each transportation mode be accurately determined, and that the survey be conducted on a "typical" weekday with favorable weather conditions.

The design of the questionnaire is an important aspect of the survey, because it will determine the amount and credibility of the returns. Attractive graphic design, with a cheerful, concise, and simple explanation of the survey purpose and method, are necessary. Questions should be kept to a minimum, and should be made simple and direct without ambiguity. The temptation to try to obtain large amounts of data with a long questionnaire should be avoided, since it discourages the completion of the

SKY COUNT SURVEY — PEDESTRIAN DENSITY CONTOURS

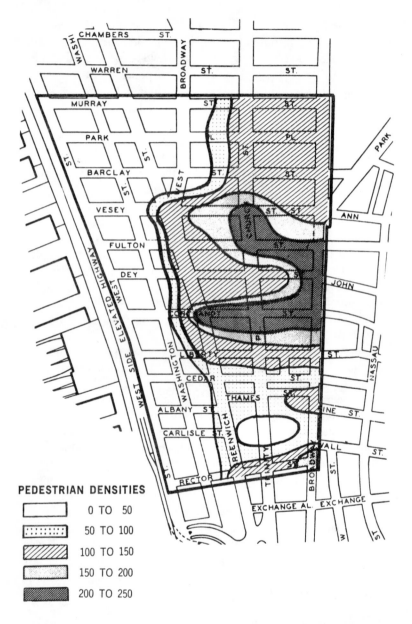

Figure 6.2

questions and, furthermore, adds to data summarization and computer coding problems. Since origin and destination returns can only be coded for tabulation by the computer into a limited number of columns and group classifications, this must be given consideration in the questionnaire design.

Origin and Destination surveys may be supplemented by a selective sampling of in-depth interviews, to obtain more specific detail on the trip maker. As an illustration, the Cleveland Downtown Agency for Transportation Action, (DATA), conducted a series of special interviews to determine user perception of the image of various districts within the city. The rationale behind these interviews was to determine if pedestrians were reluctant to walk in certain areas of the city because of negative image factors. Another technique, which is used to increase the scope of the data obtained without increasing the number of questions asked, is to distribute different types of questionnaires. All primary data requests, trip origin and destination, purpose, etc. are the same, but the remaining questions on the survey form are varied. Care must be taken to maintain dimensional control by recording the exact number of each type of questionnaire distributed and returned. At times, origin and destination surveys may involve only specific segments of pedestrian demand. For example, if the specific interest was in journey-to-work trips, only persons working in the study area might be surveyed. The advantage with this procedure is that it can be conducted with the cooperation of local businesses, and usually results in very high questionnaire return rates.

The Cleveland DATA origin and destination survey questionnaire illustrated on the following pages was designed to fold into an envelope size mail-back. Different questionnaires, with distinguishing colors, were issued to auto, bus and transit users. Questionnaires in each group were consecutively numbered to maintain dimensional control of survey populations. The questionnaire is unusually extensive for this type of survey.

CASE WESTERN RESERVE UNIVERSITY
BATTELLE MEMORIAL INSTITUTE
CLEVELAND INSTITUTE OF ART
CUYAHOGA COUNTY
CITY OF CLEVELAND
SEVEN COUNTY TRANSPORTATION LAND USE STUDY
CLEVELAND TRANSIT SYSTEM
GREATER CLEVELAND GROWTH ASSOCIATION

Project **DATA** is working to develop a **DOWNTOWN** transportation system to meet the needs and wants of all people who use the downtown area. We don't know yet what kind of system that will be. But we **DO** know that the only system we will recommend is one that Greater Clevelanders themselves have told us they want and need.

This survey is designed to show what these needs and wants are. We ask you to fill out this form and mail it in to us.

Without your help we cannot be successful in improving downtown transportation, because we won't know what improvements are needed.

With your help we **WILL** know, and will be able to set about designing the best and most convenient transportation service in the country.

All information will be considered strictly confidential. Not even the people working with the information will know its source.

THANK YOU FOR PARTICIPATING IN PROJECT DATA

GENERAL INFORMATION

1. Please print.
2. Read all questions carefully.
3. Please use **TODAY'S** information — not that of your typical day.
4. Please note every trip.
5. **PLEASE COMPLETE ALL REQUESTED INFORMATION.**
6. Please seal and drop in any mailbox — no postage required.

How often do you usually come downtown ?

Every weekday ☐   At least once a week ☐   Other _____

Home Address_____
street address or nearest intersection   City   Zip

Male ☐   Female ☐   Your Age _____

Approximate Family Yearly Income   Under $3,500 ☐ $3,500 to $6,499 ☐ $6,500 to $9,499 ☐
$9,500 to $12,499 ☐ $12,500 to $15,499 ☐   Over $15,500 ☐

Was an automobile available for you to **DRIVE** on this trip to downtown today ?   yes ☐ no ☐

Education level (circle the number which indicates the number of years completed)

Elementary	High School	College
1 2 3 4 5 6	7 8 9 10 11 12	13 14 15 16 17 18 19 20

How many trips did you make to the downtown area today ?_____

What is your occupation

☐ Professional, managerial, technical (self-employed, accountants, buyers, doctors, engineers, etc.)

☐ Clerical (secretaries, bookkeepers, tellers, etc.)

☐ Housewife

☐ Laborer

☐ Sales (salesmen, sales clerks, brokers, agents, etc.)

☐ Craftsman or Foreman (bakers, electricians, linemen, mechanics, etc.)

☐ Service worker (barbers, waitresses, janitors, policemen, etc.)

☐ Not presently employed

☐ Operative (apprentices, machine operators, truck drivers, etc.)

☐ Student

130

At what time did your trip to the downtown start today? ————————————————→ _____ _____ AM ☐
                                                                              Hour   Minute PM ☐

At what address, specific place, or nearest street intersection, **NOT RAPID STATION**, did your trip downtown start from?
_____
       street address or nearest intersection   City   Zip

How many minutes did it take you to get from there to the rapid transit station? _____

How did you get from your starting point to the rapid station:
       Auto driver ☐   Auto passenger ☐   Bus ☐   Taxi ☐   Walk ☐   Other _____

What rapid station did you go to? _____

After you arrived at the rapid station, how many minutes did you wait before you entered the rapid car? _____

At what time did you arrive at Terminal Tower? ————————————————→ _____ _____ AM ☐
                                                                            Hour   Minute PM ☐

How many people **PERSONALLY** accompanied you downtown today? _____

How many were children under 12? _____

Please list EVERY trip you made within the downtown area TODAY after leaving the bus.
WE ARE ESPECIALLY INTERESTED IN SHORT WALKING OR RIDING TRIPS.
Be sure to record return trips such as walking back to work from lunch.

EXAMPLE:

1. walk from bus stop at Prospect-Ontario to Illuminating Building to work
2. took loop bus from Illuminating Building to Boukaire's restaurant for lunch
3. walk from Boukaire's restaurant back to Illuminating Building after lunch
4. walk from Illuminating Building to bus stop at Prospect-Ontario to go home

after you left the BUS	SPECIFIC NAME or LOCATION also STREET ADDRESS if known	TRIP STARTING TIME		how many MINUTES did your trip take?	use code below	
		hour	minute		METHOD	PURPOSE
YOU WENT TO			☐ AM ☐ PM			
then to			☐ AM ☐ PM			
then to			☐ AM ☐ PM			
then to			☐ AM ☐ PM			
then to			☐ AM ☐ PM			
then to			☐ AM ☐ PM			
then to			☐ AM ☐ PM			
then to			☐ AM ☐ PM			
when you left DOWNTOWN you went to			☐ AM ☐ PM			

       street address or nearest   city
              intersection

COMMENTS:

METHOD OF TRAVEL
1. auto driver
2. auto passenger
3. bus
4. rapid transit
5. taxi-limousine
6. walk

PURPOSE OF TRIP
1. work
2. personal business
3. shopping
4. social-recreation
5. school
6. eat
7. medical or dental
8. serve passenger
9. to home
10. to car/bus/rapid

131

Analytical Modeling and Computer Simulation is being increasingly used in transportation studies because of the computers capability of handling rapidly, multiple iterations of large amounts of data. Standard computer programs are available for most of the common techniques. Their application is reasonably routine for the experienced programmer, if the proper base data is available. The computer synthesis of transportation systems is used to:

- determine the relative value of the various elements of the system, and to test the impact of changes in these values;
- forecast future system use; and to
- synthesize existing or theoretical future systems where it is not practical or possible to collect sample data.

A basic axiom of both modeling and forecasting is that large, less sensitive, conglomerate inputs generally produce more reliable results. When the inputs are more detailed, and comprised of a larger number of more sensitive variables, the results may become inconsistent for combinations of reasons that are difficult to determine. The model synthesis of transportation systems is aided by the fact that transit fares, routes, and trip times are readily determined. Auto trips are more flexible, and operating costs less obvious, so the auto trip frequently becomes the most difficult to synthesize.

Pedestrian trips are also likely to show considerable variation because of the large number of trip variables. (See Figure 6.3). During a discussion on the mathematical modeling of pedestrian trips, one analyst jokingly stated that the difficulty with the pedestrian is that at any instant he may sit down and become a non-pedestrian, or leap up suddenly and either walk or run toward any point of the compass. This may be a slight exaggeration, but it is illustrative of some of the problems connected with modeling pedestrian trips. Definitive pedestrian trip linkages, such as journey-to-work trips, are more susceptible to synthesis than lunch trips, which might also combine shopping, recreation, exercise and interest motivations.

The transient nature of pedestrian trip node and linkage combinations also tends to cause problems with some of the assumptions that are typically made in mathematical modeling. For instance, an office building is a pedestrian trip attractor during the morning journey to work, but becomes a trip generator during lunch hours.

PEDESTRIAN TRIP VARIABLES

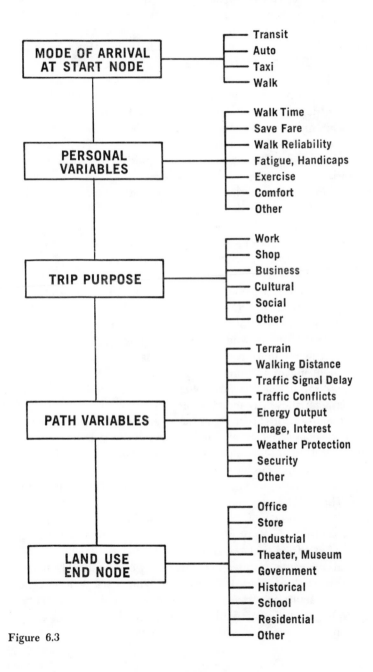

Figure 6.3

133

The base data required for the modeling process will depend on the required information output, and the modeling technique that is selected. The basic function of the model is to generate the proper number and character of pedestrian trips, and to assign these trips to the appropriate linkages in the pedestrian network. The types of data that have been used as inputs for pedestrian model synthesis include:

- Total square feet of land use by type and location, and typical pedestrian trip generation rates for each classification;
- Pedestrian income and employment categories;
- Locations of transit stops, transportation terminals, activity centers and points of interest;
- Sidewalk network distances, topographical configuration and traffic impedances;
- The volume of employee and transient populations in the study area by time of day;
- Typical pedestrian trip purpose, frequency and distance; and
- Evaluations of user perceptions of interest, security and image of various districts within the network.

Techniques that have been used for pedestrian studies include:
Gravity Models—based on the respective trip attraction and generation rates of specific districts or nodes, allocated according to an inverse square relationship with the separation of these districts in time, distance and other impedance factors.
Multiple Correlation—an empirical equation derived by the statistical fitting of a number of significant variables.
Computer Simulation—based on computer-generated trips of specific characteristics assigned to a computer-defined network.

The **Gravity Model** technique has been used in a study of the Central Business District of Toronto, Canada, to predict journey-to-work and lunch-hour pedestrian circulation demands. The data input for the model was obtained by means of an office-based questionnaire survey, using a street map of the CBD as a guide. The CBD pedestrian ways were coded into a network of centroids, comprised of transportation and office space nodes. The inputs to the gravity model were the generation and attraction rates of office and transportation zones, friction factor ratings, and minimum-path walking trees between nodes. Minimum paths were calibrated on the basis of walking time, waiting time at street intersections, street attractiveness, and a turn penalty. The model showed reasonable agreement with observed pedestrian demands at counting lines in the network.

The Multiple Correlation technique has been used by the Regional Plan Association of New York and the Cleveland DATA study. The Regional Plan Association studies developed equations for predicting the number of pedestrians in any block sector based on the area in thousands of square feet of walkway, office, retail, and restaurant space in that sector, and the distance from the sector node to the nearest transit entrance in feet. RPA derived different equations for streets and avenues, and for midday and evening pedestrian concentrations. The data input for the multiple correlation was based on counts of pedestrian generation rates at selected office, retail and restaurant activity centers, inventories of area-wide pedestrian concentrations based on an aerial photography Sky-Count survey, and classification of land use in each block sector.

The Cleveland DATA study used information obtained from an origin-and-destination survey and user perception interviews. The user perception interviews determined individual subjective evaluations of such factors as cleanliness, interest value, and image identification, of different sections of the city. The DATA model incorporated measures of satisfying trip needs at one destination as opposed to another, relative costs of different modes and combinations of modes, the numbers of different personal trip types between node points, and the spacial separation and impedances between nodes. One of the values of the multiple correlation technique is that it provides a method of testing the sensitivity of pedestrian activity to changes in one or any combination of these variables. The Cleveland model for example, allows for an evaluation of the impact of improving the user image of various districts within the CBD. This would be useful in a cost-benefit analysis to determine the relative value of such improvements.

Computer Simulation has been used for a number of small-scale pedestrian study applications, such as planning elevator service for an office building, estimating pedestrian facility demands caused by the landing of a Boeing 747, and for trip assignment to small pedestrian networks. Larger network applications have not been attempted, primarily because more complicated systems involving many trips may consume significant amounts of computer time. However, the simulation method is a simple and straightforward technique which is easily understood. Trip-maker characteristics, such as trip purpose, frequency and length, along with network characteristics, are stored in the computer.

135

The computer is then programmed to select a trip randomly, assigning specific characteristics to the trip maker on a probabilistic basis. The trip maker is then put into the trip network, advancing through it until all trip requirements are satisfied.

Improvement Programs for Pedestrians

Improvement programs may range from a basic program with very little capital expenditure, to a major program involving a complex and costly grade-separated network. Regardless of the type of program, community involvement and definitive government action is a prerequisite for success. Guidelines for different types of programs are provided in this section, but the final program for any community will depend on its own individual needs and resources. For purposes of discussion, improvement programs have been classified under separate headings, but each could be developed in varying degrees or combined with each other. The general program classifications include: **Basic Improvement Programs, Pedestrian Malls, Staggered Work Hours, Bonus Zoning,** and finally the **Major System Program.** The Elements of a **Basic Improvement Program** would be the upgrading of pedestrian safety, street lighting, pedestrian circulation, area image, and pedestrian amenities. Pedestrian safety programs concentrate on the three "E's"; Education, Engineering and Enforcement. Safety education is especially directed towards the most accident prone segments of the public, the old and the young. Special educational programs are instituted at schools and church and senior citizens' group meetings. Local news media will usually cooperate by providing advertising space, special feature stories, or television and radio spots. The American Automobile Association provides advice and special educational materials for such programs.

Engineering for pedestrian safety involves the provision of physical improvements to reduce pedestrian accident exposure. This would include standardization of signs and signals, distinctive crosswalk delineation particularly aimed at driver recognition of crosswalk zones, improving motorist lines of sight, upgraded street lighting, and any other physical features that contribute to pedestrian safety. Enforcement involves the development and implementation of legislation that protects the pedestrian, and that is uniformly recognized by both pedestrian and motorist alike.

Street lighting is an important aspect of urban design contributing to pedestrian security, safety and favorable perception of the urban image. The three-fold increase in the incidence rate of pedestrian accidents at night cited in Chapter One, is directly attributable to reduced visibility after dark. Accident and crime rates invariably decline following the installation of improved street lighting. Surveys of a number of cities instituting street-lighting improvements showed a 10 to 44 per cent reduction in all types of highway accidents and a much larger 30 to 80 per cent reduction in pedestrian accidents. In a recent survey of 1,300 police officials, 85 per cent reported a drop in local crime rates after street-lighting improvements. Half of this group described decreases of as much as 50 per cent. In one reported instance, a new street-lighting system resulted in a 70 per cent drop in criminal assaults, and a 60 per cent drop in robberies. One small town, with a population of 9,000 estimated that its better lighting was equal to the crime-deterrent value of adding four new police officers.

In addition to its safety and security value, lighting can be used to improve the pedestrian's perception of an urban space. Building facades, fountains and other attractive natural or architectural features may be floodlit to improve their appearance at night. Colored lighting can provide added visual variety. In recognition of the value of lighting, many cities have been upgrading their standards. Recommended minimums for downtown areas have been between 3 and 4 average horizontal foot-candles, (lumens per square foot). Washington, D.C., installed a high-intensity system in a high crime rate section, raising light levels to eleven foot-candles. Cleveland, Ohio quadrupled lighting levels to 8 foot-candles on two miles of its downtown streets in a program to improve their image and security. Wilmington, Delaware, upgraded a 96-block section of its downtown area to 10 foot-candles average, and the program was wholeheartedly accepted by the public and business community.

Pedestrian Circulation can be improved by sidewalk widenings, building setbacks and arcades, pedestrian connectors bisecting long blocks, proper location of street furniture, restrictions on cross-sidewalk freight operations, and traffic signalization timed for pedestrians rather than for auto traffic. The circulation improvement program begins with an inventory of sidewalk conditions in the project area, including the dimensions and locations of all permanent and movable sidewalk fixtures. The inventory may be supplemented by pedestrian volume counts to pinpoint critical sidewalk sections. Movable items, such as newsstands, telephone booths, mail boxes, and planters, should be relocated immediately if they are found to be constricting flow. Permanent fixtures, such as traffic signals and hydrants, may be moved on a long-term replacement program. An important aspect of the implementation of this program is to control the future location of these items through municipal standards and permit procedures.

Area Image and Aesthetics are important objectives of a basic improvement program. Modular design of municipal street furniture and street signs can provide significant improvements in the downtown image. A number of towns have instituted new ordinances to control the size and location of advertising signs to reduce the sign clutter that plagues many cities. Whether by municipal ordinances or on a voluntary basis, downtown merchants should be convinced that the general image of the CBD is a more important business factor than large garish signs. An aesthetic audit by a selected group of local artists and architects will pinpoint many of the more glaring violations of aesthetic design. Such a group can develop guidelines for aesthetic improvements within the framework of the existing urban structure. Aesthetic improvements may also involve restoration of buildings with distinctive architectural features or historical significance, additions of landscaping, creating small parks or plazas on unused lots, variations in sidewalk pavement colors and textures, variations in lighting, and cultural innovations such as downtown art exhibits or concerts.

Pedestrian amenities include the provision of bus shelters, covered arcades, benches and special design features for the handicapped. Ramped curbs assist the elderly, women with baby carriages and persons in wheel chairs. The elderly are specially appreciative of small "vest pocket" parks containing benches arranged in a way that is conducive to conversation. If possible, the orientation of these small parks should be based on wind protection and maximum exposure to the sun. Where possible, tactile trails should be instituted to assist the blind. The Botanical Gardens in Brooklyn, New York, maintains special "touch and smell" flower exhibits for the blind, with plant descriptions in braille. All public buildings and park facilities should be made completely accessible to the handicapped, to avoid disenfran-

Street lighting improvements upgrade area image and result in reductions in crime and pedestrian accidents.

Improved pedestrian circulation can be obtained at very little capital expense by relocating movable sidewalk impedimenta.

chising them from their citizens' rights of equal access to these facilities.

Pedestrian Malls are special street-grade pedestrian precincts, in which vehicular intrusion has either been reduced or eliminated. In many respects, the pedestrian mall is the modern equivalent of the medieval plaza, with the most successful malls duplicating the qualities of human interest, interaction and communication provided by the plaza. Because of the simplicity and small expense of closing streets, many cities have been experimenting with the creation of downtown pedestrian malls. The most successful of these experiments have concentrated on adding new features for human interest and convenience. Attractive landscaping, colorful pavement, statuary, children's play areas, and even aquariums and aviaries have been used to generate excitement and an improved image. City, state and federal assistance has partially funded many of these developments, with abutting property owners assessed for the balance. Successful malls have returned the assessment in the form of increased sales. Their most important impacts have been the revitalization of the city center, the halting of urban deterioration, and the revival of the core as a place of human interest and interaction.

The least successful mall experiments have not concentrated on providing human interest within the mall area, but have just blocked out traffic. Others have tried malls on a halfway basis, only partially blocking traffic, or not supplying adequate and convenient parking or transit access. The successful mall program must be conceived as a total system improvement which includes:

- complete exclusion of all but emergency vehicles from the mall area;
- development of an adequate perimeter street system to replace street circulation and capacity lost by the closing;
- provision of adequate peripheral access for transit, private autos, emergency and service vehicles;
- provision of adequate nearby parking, sufficient to replace all spaces lost by the street closing, plus additional parking generated by the mall;
- development of a cooperative promotional program based on building improvements, aesthetic landscaping, increased lighting, pedestrian amenities, coordinated advertising and special events.

The famous Lijnbaan, Rotterdam, Holland, a pedestrian mall that includes shopping, office and residential developments, with auto parking around its perimeter.

A proposal for a continuous pedestrian mall and people-mover system.

The types of pedestrian precincts which have been classified as malls are the following:

- **Service street or transitway**—limited-access street where cross-street traffic is allowed, but through traffic is limited to transit buses and emergency vehicles only. If service cannot be provided through rear lots, commercial vehicles must enter and leave the system by the nearest cross street. Sidewalk widening, crosswalk improvements, increased lighting levels and other amenities are added to improve the pedestrian environment. This is not a true mall, but it results in improvements in transit running times and reduced pedestrian conflicts.

- **Interrupted mall**—exclusive pedestrian street sections where cross traffic is allowed, but no vehicles are permitted on the mall sections except for emergencies. Sidewalks may be eliminated and exclusive pedestrian plazas are provided between cross streets. Service by commercial vehicles is through rear lots, or by cross-street access only.

- **Continuous mall**—an exclusive pedestrian street with no cross-street traffic, and provision for only emergency vehicles on the mall. Service is by commercial vehicles through rear lots or side streets only.

Staggered work hours—This is a concept that has evolved from the desire to reduce the severe travel peaking that occurs in central business districts due to the common work schedules of their daytime populations. Through the simple expedient of varying starting and quitting times, severe peaks are diminished, reducing pedestrian crowding in buildings, on streets, and in transit facilities. The reduction of these severe peaks not only relieves pedestrian crowding, but results in more balanced utilization of transit equipment. Business activities, such as printing, also report increased productivity, due to the longer machine-time resulting from overlapping work schedules. The most extensive staggered work hours program was instituted in the Financial District of downtown Manhattan, New York. Sponsored by the Downtown Lower Manhattan Association and the Port of New York Authority, the one-square-mile area involved in the program has a daytime employee population of about 450,000 persons. Almost all of these employees were on a 9-to-5 work schedule, with approximately two-thirds of them arriving during the peak 15-minute period of 9:00 to 9:14 A.M., and leaving between 5:00 and 5:14 P.M. In the spring of 1970, 50,000 employees of some 50 public and private organizations voluntarily changed to an earlier work schedule. A previous pilot study had revealed that no serious employee objections would be raised with a half-hour earlier or later change in work schedules, but that the earlier schedule had proved more acceptable to both staff and supervisory personnel. The earlier work schedules produced immediate results, with perceivable reductions in crowding in elevators, building lobbies and on rapid transit trains. (See Figure 6.4). A staggered work *week* has been suggested by some planners as a means of reducing urban congestion and improving the quality of life. The staggered work week would not only relieve crowding on streets, highways and transit facilities, but in over-burdened recreational areas as well.

Effects of Staggered Work Hours
PATH Hudson Terminal
P.M. Passenger Volumes

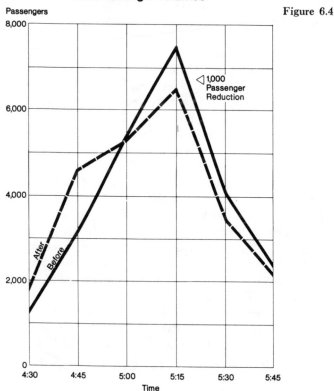

Figure 6.4

Bonus zoning—a number of cities in the United States have instituted bonus provisions in their zoning ordinances, which trade added development rights in exchange for the construction of desirable pedestrian improvements which otherwise might not be economically feasible for the developer. Because bonus provisions are not mandatory, they must be conceived to provide an incentive system which is fair, and conducive to coordination of combined public and private interests. The bonus generally offered the developer consists of adding a specific number of square feet to the allowable building area for each pedestrian improvement unit, such as an added building or subway entrance. Another method is to increase the floor area ratios by enlarging the effective lot size, or F.A.R. coverage, in some direct proportion to the area in square feet of the pedestrian plaza, mall or arcade. New York City is using a broad bonus zoning concept to preserve and promote its famous theater district. A special theater zone has been defined with the goals of protection and promotion of the character of the theater district; improving its pedestrian traffic circulation; fostering development of business and employment; providing freedom of architectural design; and providing more economic, multi-purpose construction.

The types of amenities for which development bonuses are being awarded include special uses, such as theater and historical districts, pedestrian traffic and circulation improvements and open space, and aesthetic enhancement. Pedestrian traffic and circulation improvements include sidewalk widening, multiple building entrances, access to transit or parking garages, sub-surface concourse or overhead bridge connections to other buildings or transit facilities, arcades, malls, plazas, off-street taxi and bus passenger loading areas, off-street truck berths, and shortening walking distance by mid-block connectors. The disadvantage of the bonus system stems from the lack of mandatory compliance, which results in spot, rather than continuous, system-wide improvements, and that sometimes they result in developments with questionable utility. For example, some pedestrian plazas are raised or enclosed in such a way as to limit their use for pedestrian circulation. The successful implementation of a bonus program that provides system-wide, rather than isolated spot benefits, is dependent on a well-planned and administered "carrot and stick" policy by local government.

The Major System Program represents a substantial commitment by the community and local planning and development agencies to promote a comprehensive pedestrian improvement system involving substantial capital investment. Examples of these developments, such as the elevated systems in London, Cincinnati, and Minneapolis, and the underground systems in Montreal and Toronto, are discussed in greater detail in Chapter Eight. In most instances, these developments started on a modest, localized basis, but spread rapidly as system advantages were realized. The Montreal complex began in 1962, with construction of the Place Ville-Marie shopping center. Initially, an underground linkage was provided from a below-grade shopping mall to an office building and railway station. Subsequent additions to the two-mile system were made as new building and transit stations were developed.

The London Barbican, adjacent to the heart of London's financial district, began with the redevelopment of a site that was devasted by World War II bombing. The important aspects of all these major system programs are:

- **recognition** of the importance of pedestrian circulation and amenities;
- **alertness** to every possible form of development opportunity;
- **concentration** on all the planning improvement objectives and goals discussed in this chapter;
- **commitment** to implement a substantial and continuing program.

Chapter Seven

ELEMENTS OF PEDESTRIAN DESIGN

The design of pedestrian spaces involves the attainment of the qualitative goals and objectives established in the preliminary plan, through the application of the service standards, pedestrian traffic relationships, and human characteristics contained in preceding chapters. A schematic of the elements of the pedestrian design process is given in Figure 7.1. The discussion will follow this schematic with varying degrees of amplification. The service standards and observations of the human characteristics of pedestrians contained in the previous chapters may be applied to a wide range of design situations. The purpose of this chapter is to introduce the designer to a number of these potential applications through the discussion, and by several numerical examples.

Pedestrian Traffic Demand

The ultimate design quality of a pedestrian space will depend upon its suitability and adaptability to the demands placed upon it. Demand is comprised of estimates of user traffic volumes, traffic patterns, and composition. These factors will vary according to land use, and each type may require different estimating procedures. The building and visitor populations of commercial buildings are estimated on the basis of the net usable square feet of building space. The population estimate is derived from the observed use of comparable types of space in the building locale. In large developments, where tenants may have lease commitments far in advance of final design, they will usually cooperate by providing estimates of building space occupancy, and also in conducting detailed surveys of the typical traffic patterns of their staff and visitors. Different types of commercial building uses necessarily produce different employee and visitor space ratios and traffic patterns. The main executive offices of a large corporation would have high per-person area occupancies, low visitor ratios, and less definitive traffic peaks. A service business may have low area occupancies for employee working stations, and a high visitor ratio. Retail stores would be characterized by large per-employee building areas, and very high visitor ratios. Traffic patterns also vary in different commercial building uses. A diversified-usage commercial building will have a 5-minute starting, quitting and lunch-time peak of 10 to 12 per cent of the building population. In a single-purpose commercial building, the 5-minute peak at these times may be as high as 15 to 20 per cent of the building population. Staggered work schedules, and the presence of in-house eating facilities, can lessen the severity of the peaks and provide more favorable levels-of-service.

User populations for theater and sports stadiums are directly related to the number of seats provided. Other factors involved in the design of these facilities include the adequacy of waiting areas, overlapping traffic patterns due to consecutive perform-ances, and crowd control and dispersal. The traffic pattern of these facilities is unique, in that virtually all of the users wish to depart the instant the performance or event is completed. This immediately taxes most pedestrian facilities beyond their capacity, causing delay and inconvenience. However, the tolerance level of pedestrians in such situations has been observed to be high. In designing the ancient coliseums, the Romans provided wide, open areas, or "vomitoriums," outside the Coliseum gates to absorb crowd impact and to act as an aid in the dispersal of the departing throngs. This systems approach is often overlooked in the design of modern pedestrian facilities.

The user volumes and traffic patterns of transportation facilities is usually based on a traffic forecast for some future design year. Forecasting the future of any activity is naturally beset with many potential pitfalls. The designer is encouraged to make his plans as flexible as possible to accommodate unforeseen variations in traf-fic or for unexpected demands and potential expansion beyond the initial design requirements. The typical traffic forecast is determined by a projection of past growth trends, extrapolated into the future. The designer must have a complete understanding of all the components that comprise the forecast, to assure that his design provides a high standard of service for all traffic varia-tions that are likely to occur.

Some transportation facilities are subjected to high seasonal peak demands. For example, a long-haul bus terminal in a metro-politan region will have its peak traffic demands concentrated on summer Fridays. Fourth of July and Labor Day weekends cause unprecedented demands on this type of facility, taxing it to the limit of human comfort and convenience. This peak seasonality might not be apparent from a forecast based entirely on annual growth rates. It is also possible for the peak design period to grow at a different rate than that shown by the annual forecast. The

ELEMENTS OF PEDESTRIAN DESIGN
Building and Street Spaces

Figure 7.1

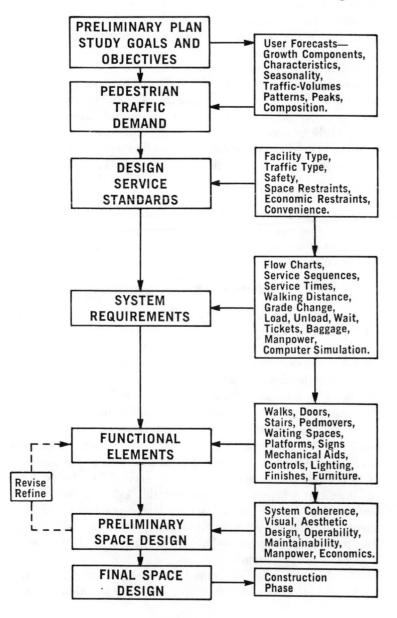

149

prospects for changing demand characteristics due to technological or regional changes must also be considered. The advent of the Boeing 747, with its transit-like volumes of deplaning passengers, is an obvious example of technological change. A not-so-obvious example is the changing operating characteristics of suburban bus routes, as the routes are extended into less dense communities. These longer routes characteristically have longer bus loading times, and therefore will usually require increased bus berth space.

Traffic composition is an important demand characteristic. Commuters that are repetitive users of the same transportation facility are likely to be more knowledgeable, younger in average age, and more agile, than the general population. They are also more likely to accept lower standards of service for short-term periods. Long-distance bus and air travellers, on the average, will be composed of less knowledgeable pedestrians, with greater proportions of the very young, the very old and the handicapped. Similar comparisons may be drawn between office-building and shopping-center populations. When traffic is composed of pedestrians that are likely to have orientation difficulties, higher standards of design, plus increased attention to system coherence, are dictated.

Application of Service Standards

The service standards in Chapter Five represent definitive verbal and pictorial descriptions of the qualitative aspects of various levels of pedestrian concentrations on walkways, stairways and queuing spaces. The service standards provide a means of either evaluating the design quality of existing facilities, or of forming the basis for the qualitative design of new facilities. The designer was cautioned that the standards are no substitute for judgement. To apply the standards intelligently, the type of facility must be established, its particular traffic characteristics fully understood, and all economic and space restraints determined. For example, it is not realistic to assume a level-of-service "A" design for a stadium exit when it is known that this exit will be instantly subjected to capacity, or "E", service levels in actual use. System clearance times, developed arithmetically, or graphically through the time-space diagram technique, are the desired measure of service in such situations.

The designer must also adjust the design section's effective width and effective traffic flow, in such a way that they are truly

PEDESTRIAN TRAFFIC PATTERNS

PER CENT OF
DAILY TRAFFIC

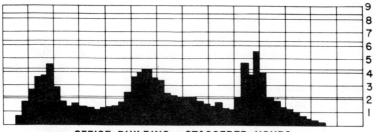

OFFICE BUILDING — STAGGERED HOURS

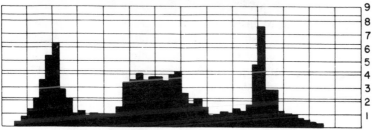

OFFICE BUILDING — CONVENTIONAL HOURS

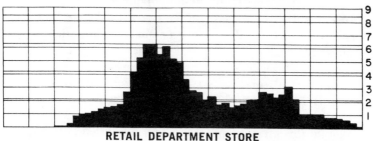

RETAIL DEPARTMENT STORE

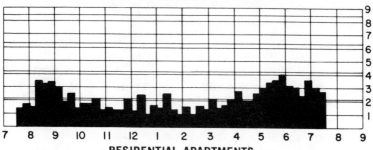

RESIDENTIAL APARTMENTS

151

representative of the type of situation depicted by the standard. This involves subtracting space for such disruptive elements as columns and sidewalk furniture, or making adjustments for interruptions of flow caused by traffic light signals or transit arrival patterns. As an illustration, it is possible that service-level area requirements may be expanded by as much as four times the established standard, to account for sidewalk width adjustments for walkway impediments and flow adjustments for traffic light cycles. The designer is also directed to look carefully for the potential weak links in the system, as the true test of design quality. Crosswalk conditions provide a more significant test of street network quality than a midblock location where traffic is stretched out and relatively free-flowing.

Economic and space restraints must receive due consideration. It is unrealistic to insist upon the highest service standards if the available physical space or financial resources are not sufficient to accommodate the design. A much better approach is to recognize the difficulties enforced by such restraints, and to seek alternative design solutions or operating procedures that will alleviate them. The one overriding consideration that precludes acceptance of economic or space restraints is pedestrian safety.

System Requirements

An optimal space design may be described as the best functional space envelope that most economically and efficiently accommodates the process or processes that occur within it. This relationship of function to design has sometimes been called "systems design", or the "systems approach". Its fundamental premise is that a thorough, detailed knowledge of system requirements leads to the most productive design. There is a good deal of logic to this premise, and, therefore, the systems approach is recommended for all pedestrian design problems. The approach begins with a detailed description of the system process in the form of a schematic diagram, or flow chart. The flow chart is supplemented with as much detail as possible that is relevant to the design decision process. If the system is large, it should be broken down into smaller sub-systems. Properly done, the system diagram becomes an invaluable reference throughout the project. It becomes the designer's checklist, and a constant reminder of the interrelationship of the various functional elements of the project. It also establishes a common understanding and rationale for all design disciplines, helping to reduce counter-productive effort.

Traffic light cycles concentrate pedestrian flow into denser platoons.

Deductions of disruptive traffic elements are required to determine effective sidewalk width.

Figure 7.2 is a system diagram for the design of a subway transit platform. This type of system may be considered rather small and limited, and not worth detailing in this manner. However, it should be remembered that a facility of this type is used by thousands of persons each day, and is expected to have a useful life of fifty years or more. It is worth the few hours required to think the system through, to determine the important elements of its design, and their individual relationship with each other. An illustrative example applying some of the factors detailed on this diagram is also contained in this chapter.

After system requirements have been described schematically, they should be described quantitatively. Often this can be done following the same basic format and sequence as the system description. Pedestrian volumes can be scaled to size and plotted graphically, to illustrate volume and direction. Pedestrian walking times, distances, and waiting and service times can also be entered on this diagram. The quantitative data, combined with directional and time relationships, is used to develop preliminary size and space configurations. At this stage of design, the plan may be very flexible, due to relatively few restraints, or it may be locked in by a more rigid set of restraints. If there are few restraints, then a large number of alternative plans may be developed. Projects with rigid restraints naturally produce fewer viable alternatives, which sometimes simplifies and shortens the design process. At times, restraints may be artificially set up on an administrative level, in an attempt to attain this objective. If these restraints are well thought out, and developed with the full knowledge and consent of the designer, they may be justified. Otherwise, they may act as a deterrent to creative and innovative solutions. The plan evaluation process must be a systematic process in which the advantages and disadvantages of each alternative is carefully assessed. This assessment is considered an important element of the creative process. The critique of even a bad plan can lead to the determination of the desirable features of a good plan. The development and evaluation process of alternative plans can be aided by various shortcuts.

One technique that is useful in plan synthesis and evaluation is to draw all stationary physical restraints, say building lines, on a base plan, and to cut out color-coded templates of all movable elements, say escalators, and shift them around the plan until a workable combination is developed. This process can be aided by mounting the base plan on a magnetic board, and affixing

SYSTEM DESCRIPTION — TRANSIT PLATFORM
Arriving Passengers

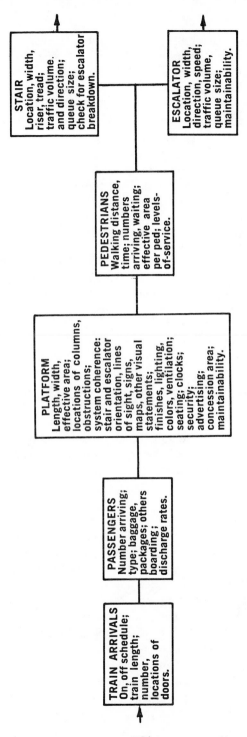

TRAIN ARRIVALS On, off schedule; train length; number, locations of doors.

PASSENGERS Number arriving; type; baggage, packages; others boarding; discharge rates.

PLATFORM Length, width, effective area; locations of columns, obstructions; system coherence: stair and escalator orientation, lines of sight, signs, maps, other visual statements; finishes, lighting, colors, ventilation; seating; clocks; security; advertising; concession area; maintainability.

PEDESTRIANS Walking distance, time; numbers arriving, waiting; effective area per ped; levels-of-service.

STAIR Location, width, riser, tread; traffic volume and direction; queue size; check for escalator breakdown.

ESCALATOR Location, width, direction, speed; traffic volume, queue size; maintainability.

Figure 7.2

155

paste-on magnetized strips to the movable elements. Rather than drafting the resulting solution, it can be recorded photographically, and the process repeated. All the plans are then projected on a screen and critiqued by the inter-disciplinary interest group. The most promising plans are formally drafted. Computer-aided design is being used increasingly to optimize plans based on pre-programmed restraints, the space requirements of various planning elements, and a weighting of desirable plan features and functional interrelationships. The computer will then develop an optimal machine solution based on these weights. Varying the weights produces alternative solutions.

Functional Elements of Building Space Design

The functional elements of the pedestrian traffic design of buildings are entrances, corridors, stairs, pedmovers, waiting spaces and directional signs. The system coherence of these elements is an important aspect of building design. Negotiating a building system is very much like a learning process. The repetitive user comprehends its configuration after a few trials, but the first-time, or infrequent, user will face difficulties if the visual components of the space are incoherent. Building configuration should be logical, containing simple, direct architectural statements that visually convey direction, orientation, and purpose to the user. A confused visual design statement cannot be solved by the addition of directional signing. Signing should be conceived as a supplementary visual aid that confirms the architectural statement rather than deciphers it.

Poor visual design statements are particularly undesirable in transportation terminal environments, where pedestrians are likely to be anxious to meet train or plane schedules, and thus are more easily confused and disoriented. Figure 7.3 is a somewhat exaggerated comparison of confused and simplified visual design, but it illustrates how incoherent design increases the need for explanatory signing, further confusing the pedestrian with multiple visual inputs, and lessening individual sign effectiveness. Simplified visual design statements do not reduce the potential for architectural variety. Variety can be obtained through variations in shapes, colors, textures, and other sensory inputs. It is worth reiterating that a pedestrian who is confused by incoherent space design is not receptive to supplementary aesthetic visual inputs. When the main concern is orientation, aesthetic input is relegated to a lower level of receptivity.

VISUAL DESIGN

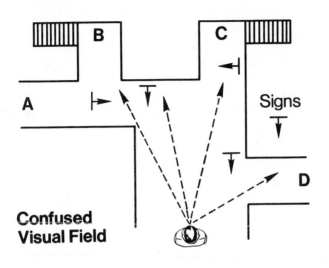

Confused
Visual Field

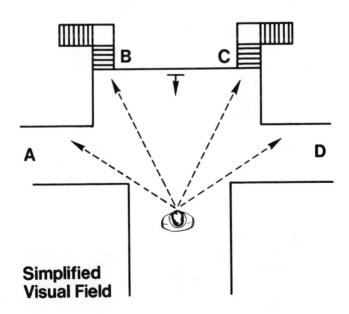

Simplified
Visual Field

Figure 7.3

157

Entrances separate and control the use of building space. Doors are used for security and to provide climate control. Doors may also be used as traffic control devices, to meter, directionalize, or channelize pedestrian flow. The Paris *Metro* has an installation of this type at its Montparnasse Station. Automatically actuated, one-way swinging doors separate entering and exiting pedestrians, to prevent conflicts between opposing traffic streams. Turnstiles are used as pedestrian-registering and revenue-control devices. The air curtain represents a departure from the control aspect of entranceways. Air curtains are used to visually integrate, rather than separate, adjoining spaces. Air curtains have the advantage that they provide for the free movement of the physically handicapped, or pedestrians with packages and other encumbrances. The inconveniences of door opening can also be eliminated by the use of mechanical door-opening devices actuated by pneumatic mats, treadles, or other types of switches. The speed of response of these automatic doors should be taken into consideration when they are used at heavy traffic locations. Also, the automatically actuated door should be capable of manual opening, in case of mechanical failure.

As discussed in Chapter Three, the design of doorways and turnstiles is based on the time needed to perform the activity of opening of the door or the registering of the turnstile, combined with an evaluation of the traffic composition and headways, or time separations, between approaching pedestrians. When traffic is composed of a large percentage of slower-reacting older pedestrians, or shoppers encumbered by packages, longer door-opening times must be assumed. If possible, doors should be set back from the walkway for both pedestrian traffic and safety purposes. A door that opens onto an active walkway is a potential accident hazard. Queuing space should be provided at the approaches to doorways, since even well-designed entranceways are likely to generate occasional queuing.

Sample Problem—Building Entrance Design

An office building developer desires to maintain level-of-service B design quality during peak pedestrian traffic periods. On the basis of net usable building area, space occupancy factors, and comparable building traffic patterns, the expected 5-minute peak exiting flow is 500 pedestrians. The architect has selected a balanced, free-swinging door that requires little effort to open. Maximum door opening and clearance time by an elderly pedestrian with packages has been observed to be 2.1 seconds. Find the number of doors, and the approach corridor width, to maintain an average level of service B design quality.

Solution

Level of service B is defined as a flow range of 4 to 7 pedestrians per foot width per minute (PFM). The upper level of the range is selected as representative of office worker traffic, because such persons are likely to be repeat users, generally younger, and more agile. The distance between door jambs is 3 feet, 6 inches, and this will be assumed to be equivalent to a pedestrian lane width.

1. Pedestrian flow per door at service level B:

$$3.5 \text{ Ft. x } 7 \text{ PFM} = 25 \text{ Peds/min}$$

2. Average headway time between Peds:

$$\frac{60 \text{ sec/min}}{25 \text{ Peds/min}} = 2.4 \text{ sec/Ped} \quad (\text{more than 2.1 sec})$$

3. Number or doors required in peak direction:

$$\frac{500 \text{ Peds}}{5 \text{ min x } 25 \text{ Ped/min}} = 4 \text{ doors}°$$

°Add 1 door for minor reverse flow — use 5 doors

4. Corridor width:

$$5 \text{ doors x } 3.5 \text{ ft.} = 17.5 \text{ ft.}°$$

°Add 2-foot-wide standing and door-opening lane, each side of corridor

$17.5 + 4 = 21.5$ feet; use 22-foot Minimum Corridor Width

Corridors and Stairs—corridors and stairs are two of the primary traffic elements of building design. The corridor dominates the space configuration because it is the axis of pedestrian movement and communication. The corridor is the unifying traffic and visual linkage between the various functional elements comprising the space, providing the pedestrian with his sense of orientation and direction. Corridor widths are determined on the basis of traffic density, and the types of activity that will occur within the corridor space, along the edges that define it, or at its end-points, or nodes. Narrow, light-traffic service corridors may be dimensioned simply on the basis of human shoulder widths, and door opening requirements.

Some designers become intrigued with the visual impact of large-scale spaces, and may attempt to obtain this objective through the use of a wide corridor. This tends to reduce the unifying effects of a corridor, reducing visual impact and the definition of its edge elements, making the pedestrian path less definitive and communicative. Although minimum corridor widths may be determined by building codes, or pedestrian traffic volumes, no guidelines have been established for the maximum widths of corridors. A corridor that requires a high amount of visual communication and interaction with its edge elements, such as in a shopping center, should have its maximum width dictated by human sight characteristics. As discussed in Chapter Two, beyond a distance of 25 feet the ability to distinguish detail is significantly diminished. This suggests that the maximum corridor width for shopping center applications should be in the 30- to 40-foot range, assuming the pedestrian walks 5 to 10 feet from the edge. A corridor this wide has a large pedestrian traffic capability, it can comfortably accommodate 10,000 bi-directional pedestrians an hour, and it could handle up to 4 to 5 times this volume if required.

The determination of the traffic capacity of corridors should be based on the net effective width, with appropriate deductions for window shopping space, column projections and other traffic obstructions. Although a corridor may be adequate for free-flow traffic, it is sometimes called upon to act as a large pedestrian holding area, or queuing space. This can occur in a transportation terminal when there is a disruption of service. Corridors that have the potential for this type of demand should be evaluated in terms of their maximum safe, and comfortable levels of pedestrian holding capacity.

As repeatedly emphasized in this text, stairs require special attention from the designer. The effectiveness of narrow stairs is very closely related to human shoulder width, and body sway requirements. Even a low-volume traffic movement in the opposite direction can reduce the effective traffic capacity of a narrow stair by half. Stairs should preferably be designed in lane-width multiples of 30 inches. Their traffic demand should be carefully analyzed in terms of direction and volume.

Because of their visual and traffic characteristics, stairs must be carefully located. The vertical projection of a flight of stairs may obstruct lines of sight to other visual elements of the space. Stairs should not be hidden for this reason. A stair represents a traffic node, and must be located in a manner that communicates direction to the pedestrian seeking an upper or lower floor. Stair location and approaches should also be designed to allow for pedestrian queuing, and to avoid conflict with other traffic streams or pedestrian facilities.

Sample Problem—Terminal Concourse Design

Based on forecasts of future passenger demand and traffic patterns, a commuter transportation terminal is estimated to have a 15-minute design peak of 5,000 passengers. During the peak 15 minutes, a short, 5-minute micro-peak, or "peak-within-the-peak", is expected to occur, which is estimated to be 50 per cent higher than the average for the design period.

Based on the estimated demand, determine the number of entrance doors, the dimensions of the main access corridor, and the number and size of stairways to serve a second concourse level. In addition, evaluate both the impact of a complete service stoppage during the design period, and the effect of the micro-peak on level of service.

Solution

Commuter transportation terminals are subject to recurrent peaks of severe, but rather short, duration. Generally they are designed for the recurring 15-minute peak, but the consequences of surges within the peak should be considered. Because the peaks are of high volumes, space is usually restricted, but their short duration and the fact that the users have knowledge of the facility justify the assumption of lower levels-of-service.

Level-of-Service C would be representative of reasonable design for a facility of this type. Traffic flows for this design level are: (see Chapter Four)

$$\text{Entrances and corridors:} \quad 10\text{-}15 \text{ PFM}$$
$$\text{Stairs} \dots \dots \dots \dots : \quad 7\text{-}10 \text{ PFM}$$

Because the users are commuters, the higher value of the range will be applied.

1. Entrance Doors

Assuming a 3-foot-wide door, the traffic volume at Level C would be:

$$3 \text{ ft. x } 15 \text{ PFM} = 45 \text{ Peds/minute}$$

this is equivalent to a headway of:

$$\frac{60 \text{ secs/min}}{45 \text{ Peds/min}} = 1.33 \text{ secs/Ped}$$

and a distance between Peds of:

$$1.33 \text{ secs x } 4.5 \text{ fps (walking speed)} = 5 \text{ feet}$$

This is rather close, but compares with observed use of free-swinging doors. Also, during heavy traffic, pedestrians may be observed holding the door for the following pedestrian, reducing clearence times slightly.

$$\text{Number of doors} = \frac{5000 \text{ Peds}}{15 \text{ min x } 45 \text{ Ped/min}} = 7.4 \text{ or } 8 \text{ doors, Major flow only}$$

8 doors + 2 for minor direction flow, use 10 doors
Minimum corridor width = 10 doors x 3 feet/door = 30 feet

2. Corridor Width

Based on building code requirements, minimum corridor width must be equal to the entrance width. However, the net corridor width, with deductions for obstructions, should be used in calculations:

$$\text{Net corridor width} = \frac{5000 \text{ Peds}}{15 \text{ min x } 15 \text{ PFM}} = 22.2 \text{ feet}$$

Add 2 feet each side of corridor for door openings and window shoppers; also add 4 feet for column obstructions.

22.2 + 4 + 4 = 30.2   Use 30 feet

3. Stairway Width

$$\text{Stair width} = \frac{5000 \text{ Peds}}{15 \text{ min x } 10 \text{ PFM}} = 33.3 \text{ feet}$$

In most modern terminals, escalators would be provided to supplement stairs. On the assumption that cost limitations allowed the installation of only three escalators operating **up**, required stair width could be significantly reduced. Based on the observed capacities of Table 5-A, virtually all pedestrians could be accommodated by the escalators. However, because this is a Transportation Terminal, the designer should consider that a power failure might put all the escalators out of service. Some agencies do not permit pedestrians to walk on stopped escalators.

On the assumption that stationary stairs will supplement the escalators, and would be used totally only during a power failure, maximum stair capacity, or level-of service "E" (17 PFM), can be assumed. The width of the supplementary stairs is:

$$\text{Stair width} = \frac{5000 \text{ Peds}}{15 \text{ min x } 17 \text{ PFM}} = 19.5 \text{ feet; Use 20 feet}$$

4. Evaluation of the micro peak:

The five-minute surge in traffic, 50 per cent greater than the 15-minute average, will cause temporary reductions in service levels and result in queuing at some service facilities.

Entrances:

The micro peak is the equivalent of a surge flow of 500 peds per minute, and the doors have been designed for a flow of:

$$8 \text{ x } 45 \text{ PPM} = 360 \text{ PPM}$$

The headway equivalent of the surge flow on the 8 doors is:

$$\frac{60 \text{ sec/min}}{500 \text{ PPM/8 doors}} = 0.96 \text{ secs/Ped}$$

the door opening and clearance time is at the maximum. A close examination of the minor flow traffic characteristics might allow for partial use of the other two doors, otherwise more doors, or alternative entrance locations, are required. The use of an air curtain entrance, the width of the cooridor, would satisfy all design assumptions.

Corridor:

The surge flow in the corridor is equal to:

$$\frac{5000 \text{ Peds x } 1.5 \text{ surge factor}}{15 \text{ min x } 22 \text{ ft. Effective}} = 22.7 \text{ PFM}$$

This flow is the equivalent of level-of-service E, which is below critical density flow, and could be tolerated for short periods without generating serious backups.

Service Stoppage:

If a complete service stoppage should occur during the 15-minute design peak, pedestrian holding space for 5,000 persons would be required on the passenger concourse. Because the waiting period is of longer duration, a minimum of 7 square feet per person, in the lower range of the human comfort zone, is recommended for evaluation of concourse adequacy.

Concourse area for service stoppage:

5,000 persons x 7 sq ft/person = 35,000 square feet

Sufficient area should be provided for this contingency in all the public open space in the terminal. If this is not possible, alternative operating procedures should be developed to prevent dangerous overcrowding.

Pedmovers create difficult design-quality decisions because of their great cost, both in initial installation and subsequent life-long operation and maintenance expense. In addition, pedmovers are large consumers of space, reducing the net area available for rental and other purposes. For example, although escalators are a desirable pedestrian convenience on a railroad platform, the penetration of the platform space by the escalator tends to disrupt queuing and flow configurations on that platform. Pedmovers act as both visual and traffic focal points for pedestrians. As a visual statement, they should be located in a way that conveys their purpose and direction. Retail stores use the pedestrian traffic channelization features of escalators and moving walks as a marketing advantage. Displays of impulse-sale items are usually located along the traffic routes linking these facilities.

Pedmovers should be related to, and integrated into, the building system to provide smooth and logical traffic flow. Clear areas must be provided at the approaches of these facilities to allow for traffic circulation, traffic mixing, and queuing. For example, banks of more than two escalators grouped side by side have been found to have lower peak capacity use because of the flow inefficiency caused by traffic conflicts at the approach section. Where space permits, banks of two or more escalators should be separated, to allow for a smooth approach transition. The designer should be familiar with traffic processes that serve the pedmover, as well as the exiting traffic process that is created by the pedmover itself. Pedestrians board an elevator individually, on different floors, but are discharged collectively, as a group, on the ground floor. After they are boarded, escalators continuously force-feed pedestrians into the landing area, whether or not that landing has the capacity or freedom of circulation to accommodate them. Readers may have observed this problem, when the leading pedestrian fails to clear the exit of an escalator or moving walk, and the following pedestrian is forced against him by the momentum of the unit.

A well-known indoor sports arena exhibits a design deficiency related to the continuous-discharge characteristic of escalators. This facility installed a multi-story system of escalators to serve several levels of the arena. At each level there is a small landing area, that must serve pedestrians leaving that level as well as pedestrians being force-fed into the area by the escalator from the floors above. When the facility first opened, dangerous crowding was experienced on the landings, and it was feared that pedestrians would be pushed through the glass walls that surround the restricted landing areas. It became necessary to institute a traffic control system using attendants, whereby flow from upper levels is periodically interrupted to allow only a limited number of pedestrians on the landing at any time. Had the arena designer properly understood the continuous, force-feed characteristics of escalators, this problem could have been anticipated. Ideally, alternative self-policing exit systems should have been provided from each level, rather than force-feeding pedestrian traffic from upper levels into lower-level traffic. Because of the significant expense of mechanical pedmovers, it is difficult to recommend a level-of-service approach. The nominal capacity ratings cited in Chapter Five represent the normal expected capacity of these units under backup queuing conditions. The designer should therefore make a detailed study of his traffic patterns, to determine maximum queue size and average and maximum pedestrian waiting times. The analytical techniques of queuing theory can be used to develop these statistics, but average values for these factors can be developed by simple arithmetic, or by use of the time clearance diagram technique illustrated in the following problem.

Sample problem—Escalator Addition

It is desired to install an **up** direction escalator at the center of a subway platform. Field counts of passengers discharged by the subway trains show that maximum traffic occurs during a short micro-peak, when two trains arrive within two minutes of each other, carrying 225 and 275 passengers, respectively. The remaining trains in the peak period are on a 4-minute headway. The platform is 900 feet long, and

15 feet wide. Evaluate pedestrian queuing and delay for the proposed installation.

Solution

1. **Escalator Capacities:**

Table 5-A, Chapter Five, contains the nominal capacities of various sizes and speeds of escalators. A maximum escalator capacity of 100 pedestrians per minute is assumed for the 120 FPM, 48 inch-wide, escalators in this example because it is a transit application with heavy arrival traffic.

2. **Construction of Time Clearance Diagram** (see Figure 7.4)

a. A graph is constructed, with time, in minutes, as the horizontal axis, and pedestrians as the vertical axis.

b. The escalator capacity of 100 pedestrians per minute is then drawn in. (The dashed sloped line).

c. The arrival rate at the escalator is a function of the train discharge time and walking time required to reach the escalator. If it is assumed that pedestrians are discharged uniformly along the length of the platform, and the escalator is located in the center of the platform, this can be approximately represented on the clearance diagram by determining the time required to walk half the platform length. A "commuter" walking speed of 300 FPM is used in this example.

$$\text{Total Arrival Time} = \frac{(\text{½ platform length}) \ 450 \ \text{ft.}}{(\text{average walking speed}) \ 300 \ \text{FPM}} = 1.5 \ \text{min}$$

The two train arrivals, of 225 and 275 pedestrians, are plotted as solid lines on the time clearance diagram.

3. **Maximum Queue Size and Maximum Wait**

Assuming all the passengers will use the escalator and not the stairs, the clearance diagram illustrates a number of significant facts. The stippled area between the pedestrian arrival rate (solid line), and the escalator service rate (dashed line), represents **total waiting time.** Division of the waiting time area by the number of arriving pedestrians gives **average pedestrian waiting time.** The maximum vertical intercept between these two lines represents **maximum pedestrian queue length.** The maximum horizontal intercept represents the **clearance interval** of the platform.

The clearance diagram shows that a maximum queue size of 75 persons would be generated by the first train arrival, if all persons seek escalator service. It also shows that 25 persons will still be waiting for the escalator service when the next train arrives. Maximum waiting time for escalator service after the first train arrival is one minute. The average pedestrian waiting time is 15 seconds. After the second train arrival, the maximum waiting and maximum queue size builds up to 1.5 minutes and 150 pedestrians, respectively. If it is assumed that pedestrians will divert to the stairs if the maximum escalator wait exceeds one minute, a one-minute-wide horizontal intercept on the graph shows that maximum queue size will not likely get larger than 50 pedestrians. This is about the limit observed for low-rise escalators of this type, where alternative stationary stairs are conveniently available.

4. Waiting Area and Platform Level of Service

At a jam area occupancy of about 5 square feet per person, 100 pedestrians in a queue require 500 square feet of waiting area. For the 15-foot-wide platform of this example, this queue would occupy about 30 to 40 lineal feet on the platform, temporarily blocking movement along this section of the platform. If the platform is the one-side-loading type, the escalator should be offset to minimize this queue interference.

The mass diagram indicates that with one train unloading, there will be a maximum of about 315 pedestrians walking along the platform and waiting for the escalator. This is an average gross area of:

$$\frac{900 \text{ feet (Length) x 15 feet (Width)}}{315 \text{ Pedestrians}} = 43 \text{ square feet gross platform area per pedestrian}$$

which is Level of Service A. The various levels of pedestrian queuing capacity on the platform are:

$$\text{(E) Danger Level:} \quad = \frac{900 \text{ ft. x 15 ft.}}{3 \text{ sq.ft./Ped}} = 4500 \text{ persons}$$

$$\text{(D) Jam Capacity:} \quad = \frac{900 \text{ ft. x 15 ft.}}{5 \text{ sq.ft./Ped}} = 2700 \text{ persons}$$

$$\text{(B) Desirable Maximum:} \quad = \frac{900 \text{ ft. x 15 ft.}}{10 \text{ sq.ft./Ped}} = 1350 \text{ persons}$$

Based on the approximate headways and passenger loads used in this problem, it appears likely that a full hour delay would be required before dangerous crowding conditions would occur on this platform. However, the preferred maximum could be reached within approximately a 15-minute delay, which would not be an unusual occurrence.

Waiting Spaces include platforms, lobbies, ticket-selling areas, baggage claim areas, or any space where the pedestrian is required to queue or wait for some service. As previously described, the amount of area required by a waiting pedestrian is a function of human space preferences and the degree of mobility or circulation required in the waiting area. Passenger platforms, or confined spaces, crowded below an occupancy of 2 square feet per person, are potentially unsafe. At this area occupancy, pedestrians can be forced through railings and other barriers, or off platforms onto tracks or roadways. A moving, but restricted queue, such as at the foot of an escalator, requires an average pedestrian area of 5 square feet per person. Where circulation through standing pedestrians is required, 10 or more square feet per person must be

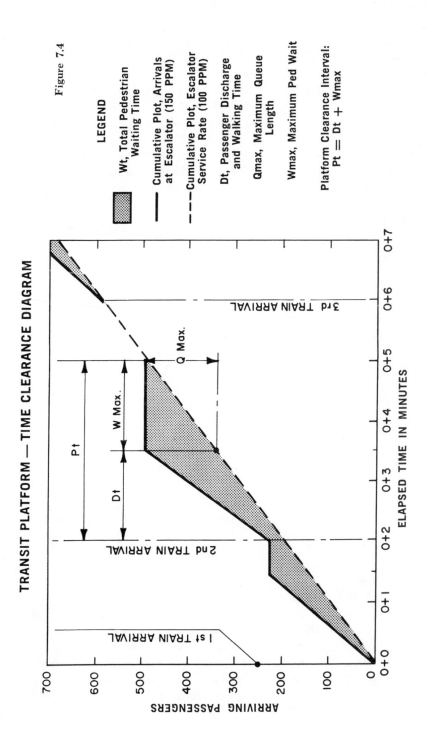

TRANSIT PLATFORM — TIME CLEARANCE DIAGRAM

Figure 7.4

LEGEND

Wt, Total Pedestrian Waiting Time

—— Cumulative Plot, Arrivals at Escalator (150 PPM)

— — — Cumulative Plot, Escalator Service Rate (100 PPM)

Dt, Passenger Discharge and Walking Time

Qmax, Maximum Queue Length

Wmax, Maximum Ped Wait

Platform Clearance Interval: Pt = Dt + Wmax

provided. Lineal ordered queues, such as on a bus waiting line, or ticket purchasing line, show a consistent spacing between pedestrians of about 20 inches. Where controlled queue lines are set up for pedestrians, using stanchions and chains or railings, the distance between stanchions should be about 24 to 30 inches. The capacity of a controlled queue line of this type, with comfortable no-contact standing, would be based on its total length, divided by the normal 20-inch queue spacing. Closer spacings could be expected in queue that are composed of persons known to each other, or where there is a degree of urgency connected with moving through the queue.

Sample problem—Airport Finger and Baggage Claim Areas

A Boeing 747 is expected to discharge up to 362 passengers in a 5-minute period. Determine the approximate finger width and baggage claim area dimensions. Evaluate the impact of the simultaneous arrival of a second such aircraft.

Solution

Assuming Level of Service A, the required minimum finger width for a single arrival would be:

$$\text{Finger Width} = \frac{362 \text{ Peds}}{5 \text{ min x } 7 \text{ PFM}} = 10.2 \text{ ft.}$$
$$\text{add 1.5 ft. clearance each side}$$
$$= 10.2 + 3.0 = 13.2; \text{ Use 15 ft.}$$

The baggage claim area should be capable of accommodating standing and circulating pedestrians. Based on queuing standard Level of Service A, the minimum claim area should be:

$$13 \text{ sq. ft./Ped x } 362 \text{ Peds} = 4700 \text{ sq. ft.}$$

The simultaneous arrival of the second aircraft would reduce the standard of service through the finger to level C, which is reasonably fluid, although somewhat crowded for this type of facility. The addition of these passengers to the claim area would introduce severe crowding, with extremely limited and restricted circulation. The claim area should be enlarged for this contingency.

Directional Signs are visual aids that help confirm the pedestrian's expectations of a space, visually communicating supplemental information and assistance. The elements of good signing are more clearly understood if directional signing is recognized by the designer as a medium for visual communication with the pedestrian. The three basic elements of signing are the **person**, or viewer, the **display**, or sign itself, and the **location** of the sign. (See Figure 7.5). When designing signs, the human capabilities of the viewer must be considered. Many of the attributes of good

ELEMENTS OF VISUAL COMMUNICATION BY SIGNS

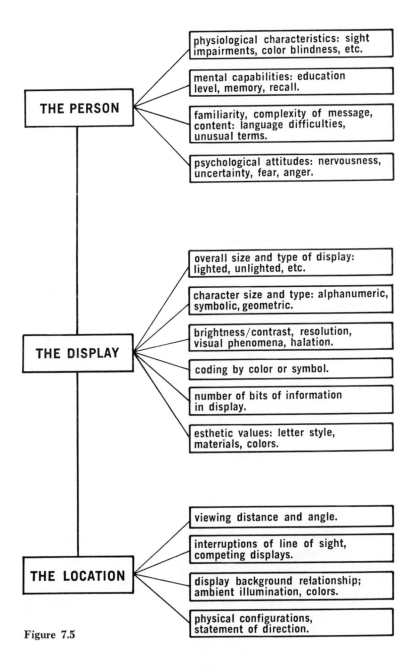

THE PERSON
- physiological characteristics: sight impairments, color blindness, etc.
- mental capabilities: education level, memory, recall.
- familiarity, complexity of message, content: language difficulties, unusual terms.
- psychological attitudes: nervousness, uncertainty, fear, anger.

THE DISPLAY
- overall size and type of display: lighted, unlighted, etc.
- character size and type: alphanumeric, symbolic, geometric.
- brightness/contrast, resolution, visual phenomena, halation.
- coding by color or symbol.
- number of bits of information in display.
- esthetic values: letter style, materials, colors.

THE LOCATION
- viewing distance and angle.
- interruptions of line of sight, competing displays.
- display background relationship; ambient illumination, colors.
- physical configurations, statement of direction.

Figure 7.5

signing can be compared to the factors that enhance human short-term memory. Short-term memory is improved by rehearsal, or introduction to the terms and conventions of the signing system; use of short, familiar, and consistent terms; avoidance of the need to translate the sign message into other units, terms or meanings, reducing the number of individual terms or bits of information to be assimilated; use of repetition to improve confidence, and continuity and consistency of sign format and means of presentation.

It should be recognized that there are different degrees of learning required by signs. Complicated, color-coded signing systems can confuse the pedestrian if he has visual deficiencies, insufficient time, or lacks the mental ability to learn the meaning of the code. An estimated eight per cent of the adult population is subject to color confusion, and many others have functional illiteracy, or the inability to understand complicated instructions reducing the effectiveness of elaborate signing systems. The display or sign itself should be easily recognized by the pedestrian as a directional sign. Distinctive graphic design, involving the use of modern type faces, easily identified logos or other symbols, and consistent format, will help identify directional signing and avoid confusion with other types of signs. A rule of thumb for directional sign lettering height is a letter-size minimum of 2 inches, plus one additional inch of letter height for each 25 feet of viewing distance. In other words, a sign that is to be viewed from a distance of 50 feet should have at least a 4-inch letter height.

Sign location can be a significant communication factor. The sign should have clear, unobstructed lines of sight, and good viewing angles. A 30-degree viewing angle is considered the optimum for reading a sign. Competing visual displays, or a confused background, can reduce the effectiveness of signing. Similarly, improper backlighting, or reflective glare off the sign face, can significantly reduce its communication value.

The Design of Street Spaces

The functional components of the traffic design of street spaces for pedestrians include sidewalks, street furniture, and street lighting. The street network is both the spinal column and the circulatory system of urban space, providing it with its structure and viability. Streets are linkages between the various functional components of the city, the arteries through which flows the city's life-sustaining fluid of people and goods. The mark of a robust and growing city is a well-defined and functionally designed street system.

Sidewalks are the pedestrian's portion of the street space. The pedestrian must share this space with countless pieces of hardware and furniture, much of which is required for the traffic control of vehicles. In addition to this intrusion into the pedestrian's space, the utility and continuity of the sidewalk system is reduced further by vehicular conflicts, and signal systems which are timed to favor vehicles. When designing or evaluating sidewalks, deductions must be made for the incursions by street furniture and time interruptions by signal cycles. There are other considerations involved in the determination of effective pedestrian space on sidewalks. Many new buildings have taken advantage of zoning bonus provisions, and have provided pedestrian plazas. When these plazas are properly integrated with the sidewalk, they may be positive additions to effective pedestrian space. However, there are examples of plaza development where the plaza has been segregated from the sidewalk by walls, decorative planters, or grade discontinuities, which have negated the potential pedestrian space advantages of the plaza. Other design features

Pedestrian plazas with grade discontinuities do not benefit sidewalk traffic.

limit the effectiveness of sidewalks from the human factors stand-point. Curb heights may be set too high for convenient human locomotion. Curb height should be no greater than the normal stair riser height maximum of 8 inches. Preferably, curbs should either be set at 7 inches or less, or ramped, to facilitate use by the handicapped. Because of sight limitations, locomotion handicaps, or just convenience, many pedestrians may be observed to bypass raised-curb safety islands, walking instead into active traffic roadways, to avoid stepping up and down. Walk-through islands channelize pedestrian flow, and eliminate this practice. Sidewalk gratings similarly inconvenience many pedestrians because of their slippery surfaces and the tripping hazards caused by openings in the grating.

Sample problem—Sidewalk Evaluation

A new office building is expected to add 2000 additional pedestrians in a 10-minute period to (A) an existing sidewalk, (B) a crosswalk holding area, and (C) an existing subway stair. (See Figure 7.6). The traffic light cycle at the crosswalk is 60 seconds, with a 25/35 split favoring the avenue. Evaluate levels of service at points (A), (B), (C), and the crosswalk (D).

Solution

(a) Sidewalk Section:

The effective width of sidewalks must be reduced because of street furniture, light standards and other obstructions. Assuming a five-foot reduction, the pedestrian volume, (P), per foot of sidewalk width, per minute, is:

$$P = \frac{3000 \text{ Peds}}{10 \text{ min x } 15 \text{ ft.}} = 20 \text{ PFM}$$

From the level-of-service design chart in Chapter Four, the level of service at this volume is E, and the approximate effective area per pedestrian is about 10 square feet. At this level of service and area occupancy, walking speeds, reverse flows and cross movements would be severely restricted.

(b) Crosswalk Hold Area:

With the 25/35 traffic signal split, the crosswalk holding area would be required to queue, on the average:

$$\frac{1500 \text{ Peds x } 25 \text{ sec}}{10 \text{ min x } 60 \text{ sec}} = 63 \text{ Pedestrians}$$

The required queuing area for these pedestrians, based on a queuing standard of 5 square feet per pedestrian, is 315 square feet, or the entire area at the corner of the building. These queuing pedestrians will block sidewalk access to the side street.

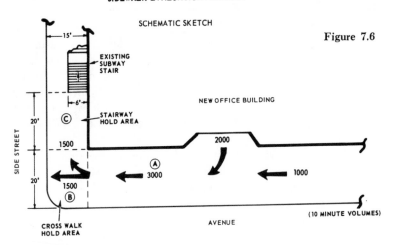

SCHEMATIC SKETCH

Figure 7.6

(c) Subway Stair:

The existing subway stair will be saturated by the added pedestrians. Assuming the absolute maximum design value of 20 PPM per ft. width of stairway, a queue of 30 PPM will build up, growing to a length of 300 or more pedestrians in the ten-minute design period, completely exceeding the small hold area behind the stair.

The saturation of the existing stair and pedestrian holding spaces make it mandatory that the office building developer be required to provide supplemental stairway connections to the subway. These connections should be made directly through the building to minimize the increase in sidewalk volumes.

(d) **The Crosswalk**

The 1500 pedestrians crossing the street during the ten-minute office building peak will actually be concentrated into denser platoons because of the interruptions of the traffic light signal. The available green time for pedestrians is 35 seconds out of each minute. The pedestrian requires an additional 3 seconds for perception and reaction time, further reducing his available green time. The average flow approaching the crosswalk is 150 pedestrians per minute. The concentrated flow crossing after the green indication is equivalent to 150 pedestrians in 32 seconds. The resultant level of service on the crosswalk due to this platooning is determined as follows:

$$P = \frac{150 \text{ Peds x } 60 \text{ sec}}{32 \text{ sec x } 15 \text{ ft. sidewalk}} = 18.7 \text{ PFM}$$

This is the equivalent of level of service D, in the range of severely restricted flow. This does not include traffic volumes that may be added from the side street, or conflicts caused by pedestrians standing and at the corner waiting to cross the avenue.

173

Street Furniture is comprised of an endless list of impedimenta all deemed to have some proprietary or pre-emptory right over the pedestrian's sidewalk domain; parking meters, mail boxes, refuse cans, fire hydrants, fire alarm boxes, planters, newsstands, subway kiosks, telephone booths, bus shelters, signs, signals, light poles, etc., etc. Other sidewalk impedimenta not included in the furniture category are house steps, storage cellar entrances, and the sidewalk cafe. The latter may contribute to local color, but it is invariably located at the corner, in the midst of crosswalk confusion.

There has been little, if any, regulation of the location of these sidewalk incursions. The improvement of this sorry picture is dependent upon strong municipal action. All supplementary uses of sidewalk space must be carefully controlled. Efforts must be made to reduce the number of these uses by incorporating different elements into attractively designed modular units, simplifying municipal regulations to reduce signs, and restricting private uses of public sidewalk space. Sidewalk furniture should be eliminated entirely at crosswalks that are narrow and subjected to heavy traffic demand.

Street Lighting is one of the most important design components of the pedestrian's environment after dark. High levels of illumination have been found to reduce pedestrian accidents, and to improve pedestrian security and area image. Minimum recommended illumination for urban downtown areas is as follows:

Roadway Classification	Minimum Average Horizontal Footcandles (Lumens per foot)
Major street	2.0
Collector street	1.2
Local or minor	0.9

Many cities have significantly upgraded their illumination standards in downtown areas by as much as four to five times the recommended minimum. These improvements have been supported by the local citizens who have, in many instances, willingly paid additional tax assesments to upgrade lighting levels. Lighting levels are dependent on the type of luminaire (the lamp and its reflective devices), its mounting height, and the spacing of supporting poles. Illumination on the lighted surface decreases inversely as the square of the distance from the light source. Because of this inverse square law, the primary problem in lighting design is to obtain as uniform a distribution of light on the street surface as possible.

This balanced light distribution is based on the use of luminaires with the most efficient lighting patterns for the particular space, and by spacing lighting poles for efficient overlapping of lighting patterns. If light poles are spaced without this overlap, an uneven brightness occurs. Ideally, light poles should be spaced so that the illumination from one complements the other, to produce an even brightness level. Street lighting can be enhanced with floodlighting of pedestrian crosswalk areas and special interest features, such as statues, or architecturally attractive buildings. Some area features that appear relatively drab in the daylight environment can be considerably enhanced by floodlighting them at night.

Pedestrian Walking Distances

Walking distances, are important because they are a factor in plan configuration, and a measure of design serviceability. Unfortunately, walking distances are a subjective human variable, with relatively long walking distances being accepted under some circumstances and rejected under others. Studies of walking trips in downtown CBD's usually reveal a large number of trips which total only a few hundred feet. Sometimes this data is used to justify moving-sidewalk installations for the longer walking-trip distances, say above 1000 feet. It should be noted that many of the short walking distances in CBD's are related to its dense development, and the increased likelihood that more trip nodes will be closer to each other. In addition, the value of time is likely to be accentuated more heavily in the CBD, because of the requirements of meeting work and lunch schedules, and this reduces the time available for walking. The CBD might be contrasted with an amusement park, or a world's-fair type of situation, where walking distances in thousands of feet, and even miles, are tolerated.

An origin-and-destination survey of passengers departing from the Port Authority Bus Terminal, in midtown Manhattan, disclosed that one-third of the passengers using the terminal walked from their origins, and that the average walking distance for these persons was about 3500 feet. This high average walking distance can be attributed to a number of factors, including: (1) that the survey was conducted during the spring, in fair weather; (2) that the long, rectangular grid pattern of Manhattan streets increases path lengths; (3) that walking is free; and (4) that walking times are more predictable than the combined total of waiting, transfer, and trip times of Manhattan bus, taxi, and transit facilities.

The origin-and-destination survey results provided the data for developing a relationship between walking distance and the proportion of Bus Terminal passengers who walk or use other transportation modes. The relationship is shown in Figure 7.7. The data used to develop this diversion-curve form of relationship was found to vary according to transit convenience. Zones with poor transit service were found to have a higher proportion of walkers. The Terminal passenger diversion curve shows that for up to about a 1000 feet from the Terminal virtually all persons walked; up to one mile almost 50 per cent walked; and two miles was the practical walking limit. The persons in the survey were almost all commuters, representing more of the healthy, non-handicapped segment of the general population. It is known that some of these persons will also walk in pleasant weather, as a means of exercise.

These rather long walking distances compare with the shorter, but severely criticized, maximum walking distances at major airports. Maximum walking distances from curbside to planeside have been reported to be 1735 feet at O'Hare Airport, Chicago; 1730 feet at Atlanta; 1650 feet at Dallas; 1300 feet at San Francisco International; and approximately 1100 feet at the Los Angeles International, John F. Kennedy International, Miami and Detroit Airports. Inter-terminal distances at these airports were found to vary from 2000 to almost 8000 feet.

There are indications that the tolerable limit of human walking distance is more situation-related than energy-related. The maximum curb-to-plane walk distances represent a normal 5- to 7-minute walk for most persons, but the anxiety connected with meeting schedules, making the trip, and negotiating an unfamiliar building, tend to make these distances appear to be much longer. The tolerable walking distance for a given design situation is related to such factors as the trip purpose of the individual, available time, and the walking environment, rather than energy consumption. This strongly suggests that improvement of the design environment to reduce negative psychological factors is as important as reducing pedestrian walking distances.

176

PEDESTRIAN WALKING DISTANCE
Bus Terminal Passengers

Figure 7.7

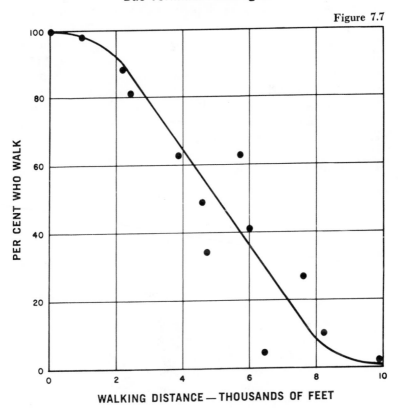

PER CENT WHO WALK

WALKING DISTANCE — THOUSANDS OF FEET

Designing for Handicapped Pedestrians

The objective of making pedestrian facilities accesible to, and usable by, the physically handicapped, provides direct benefits in improved utility and service to all pedestrians as well. Handicapped pedestrians report that they are apprehensive of the dense, irregular, and usually hurried pedestrian traffic in most travel situations. One reason for this apprehension is the fear of actual physical impact with other pedestrians, who may not be aware of their handicaps, and another is their acute awareness that their slow pace may be impeding the progress of others.

Higher level-of-service design standards for walkways would help to relieve many of the apprehensions of the handicapped, by providing sufficient area for all pedestrians to select their desired pace. Handicapped persons also experience difficulties with high riser heights on stairs, and projecting stair nosings. Reduction of riser height provides a stair that is negotiated with a greater degree of traffic efficiency and convenience. Rounded stair nosings reduce tripping hazards for the non-handicapped. Public transportation systems and public buildings must devote increased attention to accomodating the handicapped to assure them the full enjoyment of their citizen's rights to use these facilities.

Minimum Recommended Design Standards to Make Facilities Usable for the Handicapped Pedestrian
(Based on ASA Standard A117.1–1961)

Walks
- Walks should be at least 5 feet wide, with a maximum grade of 5 per cent. Walks with greater than a 5 per cent grade are considered ramps.
- Walks should be of a continuing, common surface, not interrupted by steps or abrupt changes in level.
- Wherever walks or roadways cross, the pavement should be cut, and the walk ramped to road level.
- Where walkway systems are frequented by the blind, or where walkways cross streets, changes in pavement texture should be used, to provide the blind with tactile signals of route, and crossing, locations.
- Longer walks near the maximum grade should have level areas at intervals, for purposes of rest and safety.
- Walks should have non-slip surfaces.

Ramps
Where ramps are provided, the following minimum standards should apply:
- Ramp slopes should not exceed a slope greater than 1 inch per foot, or 8.33 per cent grade.
- Ramps should have handrails on at least one side, and preferably on both sides, extending at least one foot beyond the ends of the ramp. Handrails should be set at a height of 32 inches, measured from the ramp surface.
- Ramps should have non-slip surfaces.
- Ramps should have level platforms at 30-foot intervals, and

Pedestrians are more likely to use convenient walk-through safety islands.

Ramped curb cuts at cross walks assist the handicapped.

at ramp ends for rest and safety. Where a door opens on the ramp end, minimum platform dimensions must be at least 5 feet by 5 feet, or sufficient to allow door opening and wheelchair maneuvering.

Entrances

- At least one primary entrance to each building should be usable by persons in wheelchairs. This entrance should be on a level accessible to building elevators.
- The location of this entrance should be indicated by an appropriate sign or symbol.
- Doors should have a clear opening of no less than 32 inches, free of protruding hardware. (See Figure 7.8).
- Sharp inclines, or abrupt changes in level, should be avoided at doorsills. Floors on the inside and outside of each doorway should be level for a distance of 5 feet in the direction of the door swing, and for at least one foot of width on each side of the door.
- Doors should be operable with a minimum effort. Door closers should be of the type that does not require much effort for opening, and which close slowly enough to allow for uninterrupted passage of a wheelchair.

Stairs

- Stairs should have plain faces. Open riser stairs, or stairs with edges projecting out over the face of closed risers, are not recommended. (See Figure 7.9).
- Maximum riser heights should be 7 inches; preferred riser heights would be between 5 and 6 inches. Tread width should be at least 11 inches.
- Handrails should be set at 32 inches, measured from the tread at the face of the riser, and should extend 18 inches beyond the stair ends.
- All treads should be of non-slip surfaces.
- Stair lighting should be a minimum of 5 foot-candles on the average; preferred lighting levels should be above 10 foot-candles on the average.

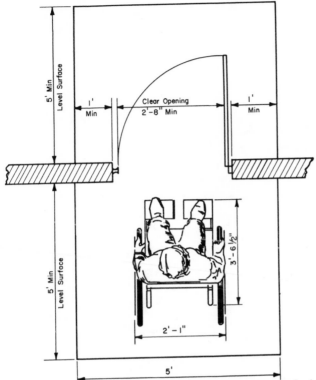

Entrances should be designed to facilitate maneuvering of wheelchairs.

Figure 7.8

1. RECOMMENDED   2. NOT RECOMMENDED   3. NOT RECOMMENDED

Rounded stair nosings are preferred. Open back stairs and stairs with projecting nosings cause locomotion difficulties for the handicapped.

Figure 7.9

Chapter Eight

NEW DEVELOPMENTS IN PLANNED
PEDESTRIAN ENVIRONMENTS

A new age is dawning for the pedestrian: a return to the human scale of the cities of the past; an awareness of the need for human interaction and communication; a realization of the importance of the human sense of belonging to, and relating with, the design environment. It stems from the recognition that a space should serve its users free of the incoherence and confusion of conflicting purposes. Its evolution in the cities began with the first, small-scale pedestrian mall experiments. Its evolution in buildings began with some of the more innovative air passenger terminal designs. Planners and designers around the world are awakening to its promise. The examples cited in this review have been selected for illustrative purposes.

The London Barbican—Out of the Ashes

During World War II, bombs devastated a large area adjacent to the downtown section of the city of London. Because of its proximity to the downtown financial district, the area could have been easily reconstructed with high-density office building developments. However, the area is rich in historical importance, dating back to the days of the early Roman occupation. The magnificent dome of St. Paul's Cathedral, designed and built by Christopher Wren after the great London fire of the late seventeenth century, is the dominating landmark in the area.

Instead of more office buildings, the Corporation of London built the Barbican, a combined cultural and residential complex designed to serve the needs of the business district, and to preserve the historical significance of the area. The Barbican contains 2,113 flats, maisonettes, and terrace houses, for up to 6,500 residents; a 200-room hotel for students and young city workers; the new Guildhall School of Music and Drama; a theater; an art gallery; a concert hall; a cinema; a library; shops; restaurants and pubs. The development is served by a segregated system of elevated pedestrian walkways, with roads, truck service bays, and parking below, out of sight of the pedestrian level.

The network of elevated pedestrian ways connects directly with the financial district, so that it is possible to live, work and enjoy all the area's cultural advantages without vehicular conflict. The elevated plazas have been attractively landscaped, and particular care has been taken to maintain and enhance the vistas of historic St. Paul's. An ancient Roman wall, perhaps 1,500 years old, presents an unusual interest feature at one location. The Barbican is an excellent example of human scale design, and the preservation and enhancement of the sense of place, or space image.

Above and upper right, the elevated walkways of the Barbican, in the heart of the City of London.
Lower right, plan of Barbican development and connecting walkway system.

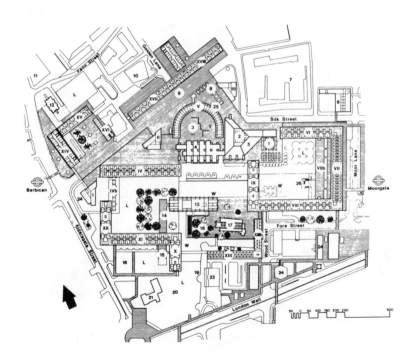

Montreal and Toronto—Pedestrian Subways

Both Montreal and Toronto, Canada, have embarked on programs to establish pedestrian networks beneath their central business districts. The Montreal system began in 1962, with the development of the Place Ville-Marie shopping mall and its associated forty-two-story office tower. Underground linkages were built between the Place Ville-Marie complex and the nearby Canadian Railway Station and Queen Elizabeth Hotel. The initial small-scale network proved so popular that subsequent linkages were made to other large developments in the area. In 1971, the system totaled approximately two miles of connecting pedestrian passageways, serving forty acres of prime office, hotel and retail stores, including three hundred underground shops, fifty restaurants, and twenty-five-hundred hotel rooms.

The underground network is completely enclosed, and climate-controlled in both summer and winter. This is most appreciated during the rigorous Canadian winter, allowing the pedestrian to avoid the cold and slush above. A reduction in downtown-district pedestrian accidents has also been noted since its inception, which has been attributed to the reduction of pedestrian-vehicle conflicts. Montreal's system is largely unplanned, and there is no overall master plan. Each developer initiates his own plans, and the total network is somewhat deficient because of it. There is also a lack of visual relationship with surface elements, which affects the imageability of the system. The City Planning Department has initiated studies and developed concepts for a more coherent system for the future.

Toronto's underground pedestrian circulation system is less developed than Montreal's, but a completed downtown network is envisioned by 1980. The Toronto concept is similar to that of Montreal, linking major generators, such as shopping centers and hotels, with transportation nodes. The Toronto system is also dependent upon individual developers, but there has been active participation by city planners and partial funding by the City. The Toronto Transit Commission which owns and operates the Metro system has also taken an active part in the development, promoting direct linkages to subway stations and major traffic generators in the system. Toronto planners are convinced that the total image of the city and its ability to attract new investment is dependent in a large measure on the ease, freedom and pleasure with which pedestrians can move about. Profiting from Montreal's

Illustration of store front development in Montreal underground pedway system.

Aesthetic treatment of a pedestrian subway in the Montreal system.

experience, they have attempted to increase the imageability of the underground network, opening it to the street environment above. This has limited opportunities for climate control, but has contributed to an increased variety of visual experiences. Plans for the proposed Metro center, an air-rights development above the National Canadian Pacific Union Station, which would have 20,000 residents and 40,000 daytime workers, include provision for visual relationship with the underground pedestrian network. The visual orientation of the pedestrian has been considered in the design of the Center's approaches from the underground network. Outdoor courtyards, entrances, and building shopping ways may all be encompassed in a single gaze.

Cincinnati and Minneapolis—Pedestrian Skyways

The cities of Cincinnati, Ohio, and Minneapolis, Minnesota, have embarked on programs for aerial walkway networks in their downtown central business districts. Unlike Montreal and Toronto, the two cities have no underground subway system to integrate with, allowing the freedom to choose the less expensive skyway alternative. The overhead systems have the advantage that they can be built quickly, without conflict with underground utilities or surface traffic. Also, the overhead systems allow a clearer visual relationship with the elements of the cityscape. However, the design of aesthetically attractive bridge connections between buildings is a challenge to the architect and structural engineer. Elevated street bridges in Minneapolis have been constructed of prestressed concrete, with finished steel railings and tinted glass paneling enclosures. Maximum use has been made of glass and high levels of lighting for security purposes. Although all skyways have not been climate-controlled, provision has been made for this eventuality.

The Cincinnati system interconnects 10 square blocks in the heart of the downtown district. An additional spur serves Cincinnati's 56,000-seat lakefront sports stadium. The Cincinnati skywalk system is being developed with a combination of private, municipal and federal financing. Plans for pedestrian circulation within the core recognize the need to walk quickly, and unencumbered by vehicular conflict, between major pedestrian traffic generators. The second-level walkway system connects the city's retail section, and a showcase concentration consisting of the convention hall and hotels on the west, the office building concentration on the east, and the lakefront stadium on the south.

PLANNED DEVELOPMENT OF CINCINNATI
ELEVATED SKYWAYS

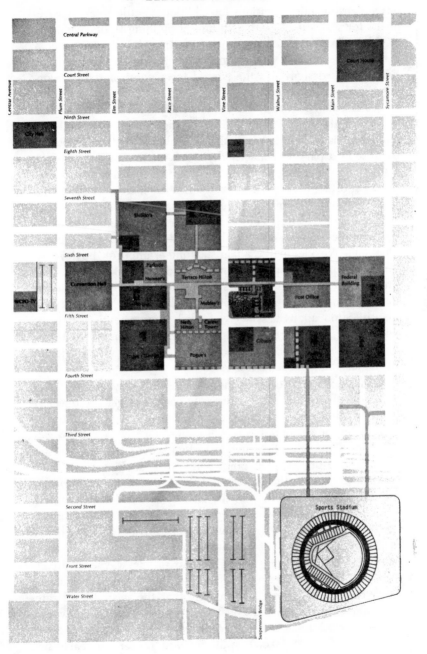

An added moving walk linkage to the Stadium has been considered because of long walking distances from the CBD. The city's plans include provisions for additional grade-level improvements for pedestrians, with arcading of building fronts, widening of sidewalks and the improvement of street furniture design. A pedestrian mall, containing Cincinnati's historic Tyler Davidson Fountain, is designed as the central focal point of the development. (Block "A" on map).

The elevated connection to the lakefront stadium has proven to be one of the most valuable links of the system. Originally intended to make downtown parking available to stadium spectators because of a parking capacity deficiency at the stadium itself, it brings large numbers of these persons into the downtown area during sporting events. This has significantly increased downtown restaurant and shopping business volumes on these days.

Minneapolis, Minnesota, has the distinction of being one of the most people-oriented cities in the United States. It's famed eight-block-long Nicollet mall is an outstanding example of the development of a prime retail street into a visually exciting pedestrian precinct, where private vehicles are banned. Although the Nicollet mall development is significant by itself, the ambitious skyway plan of Minneapolis has received much more attention. It is expected that, by 1985, 64 pedestrian bridges will connect 54 blocks of the downtown CBD. An additional 13 blocks will be joined by underground concourses.

Minneapolis city officials began studying elevated walkway systems as early as 1958, but literally could not get the development "off the ground" because of merchants' concern for potential loss of business from street-level stores. Finally, a few private developers thought that such a system would be economically feasible, and proved their point when the first skyway was built in 1962 as part of the Northstar Center development. Property values immediately soared in the vicinity of the Center, persuading a number of businesses to remain downtown instead of moving to the suburbs. Five more skyways were privately financed and built, linking a total of 16 downtown buildings.

Instead of decreasing rental values, the skyway and arcade system increased the rental receipts of the second level of the connecting buildings so significantly that the second-level rates now approximate the rates on the street floor, without lowering street-floor values. Costs of skyways have been suprisingly low, averaging about $100,000, split between owners on each side

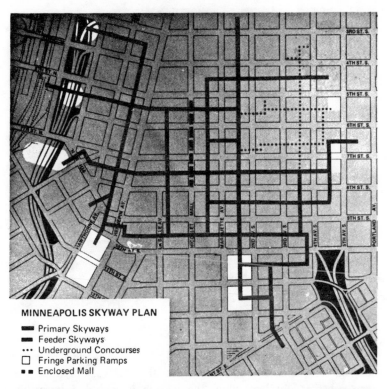

MINNEAPOLIS SKYWAY PLAN

Primary Skyways
Feeder Skyways
••• Underground Concourses
☐ Fringe Parking Ramps
■ ■ Enclosed Mall

View of two Minneapolis Skyway bridges.

191

Interior design of a Minneapolis Skyway.

of the street. Remodeling of second-story arcades has proven to be more expensive than the skyways themselves, but these costs are substantially less when the arcade is included in original construction.

The guidelines for the skyway system development adopted by the Minneapolis Planning and Development Department include provisions for adequate walkway dimensions, pedestrian comfort, security, and imageability. Minimum clear walkway widths are set at 12 feet, and preferably 20 feet, for connections to major traffic generators. Minimum headroom is set at eight feet. Unobtrusive design is recommended for all skyways, and arcades. Additional recommendations include climate control, and a use of glass and high lighting levels for "openness" and security. Pedestrian access and use of the system is to be facilitated by good signing, and clearly marked entries from street level. The skyways and arcades will make use of multi-level courts and open spaces, to visually link the street with the second-level system. Every effort to introduce interest and variety along the route of the system is advocated. Standardized structural design and details are recommended to simplify skyway construction and to reduce costs.

Boston—A Moving Skywalk for Downtown

The Boston Redevelopment Authority recently completed a detailed study of an internal distribution system for its downtown area under a $200,000 technical study grant from the Urban Mass Transportation Administration. The extremely thorough study included determination of downtown transportation requirements, engineering feasibility of various systems, definition of design objectives, and an evaluation of legal considerations. The design objectives of the system include: improvements to pedestrian mobility and convenience; reduction of crowding at existing stations; flexibility and adaptability to change; reliability and maintainability of equipment; safety; security and comfort; the achievement of a sense of place and community; enhancement of property values and encouragement of new development; accessibility to the system; creation of a strong, easily identified urban structure; and a favorable cost-to-benefit ratio.

As a result of the study, it is proposed that a weather-protected system of elevated moving walks be constructed along two routes, 2,500 and 1,400 feet in length. Parallel, stationary sidewalks would be provided for those who do not choose to use the moving walk. Conventional, constant-speed units were recommended for initial installation because of commercial availability and demonstrated reliability. Variable-speed systems were found to be mostly experimental and untested. The moving walks system was selected because it combined the advantages of continuous automatic operation, low operating costs, high capacity, and safety. In addition, moving walks may be reversed, to handle peak demands.

Another factor that was considered is that moving walks require very little space, and their use bears a strong resemblance to walking, thus helping the creation of a pedestrian-oriented environment. Mini buses were considered for CBD distribution, but were rejected because of capacity limitations, high operating costs, requirements of street right-of-way, and space for storage and repair. Other "people-mover" system, such as Carveyor, Dashaveyor, Starrcar and Minirail, were also considered, but were judged inappropriate for the particular short-distance application, for either low capacity, incompatible operating characteristics, high cost, or aesthetics.

An interesting aspect of the study was a state-of-the-art investigation of variable-speed moving walks. Six concepts for accelerating walks were considered and compared with current constant-speed equipment. The concept found to have the best potential for this application was a "multiple belts linear array system", comprised of a series of constant-speed belts in a linear sequence, each belt longer and faster than its predecessor. The main, or fastest-speed belt, would be travelling at 4.4 miles per hour, approximately 50 per cent faster than normal walking speed, and four times faster than current moving-walk speeds. The study indicated that if experiments prove the feasibility of this sequential acceleration system, it can easily replace the proposed constant-speed system.

A scale model of Boston's proposed elevated moving skyway.

Underground Atlanta—"Hidden Gold"

Atlanta, Georgia, literally discovered hidden gold beneath its doorstep with the development of a small, but unique, high-interest pedestrian precinct below its downtown area. The town of Atlanta has always been an important southern rail hub, with rail lines converging on its downtown area. In 1834, a bridge was erected over the railroad to facilitate downtown traffic movement. This first grade-separation improvement was so successful that Atlanta instituted a program to elevate all its downtown streets above the railroad terminal area. This undertaking was so extensive it took almost a century to complete. After the building of the elevated viaducts, the streets below were shut off from commercial activity, so the merchants boarded up the fronts of the old buildings and moved their operations up one level. For approximately seventy years, these old store-fronts remained dormant, while the city above flourished. However, the forgotten city below was the scene of most of Atlanta's early history. In 1967, Underground Atlanta Incorporated was formed by a group of enterprising Atlantans to bring this historic area back to life. The company undertook the restoration of four square blocks of sub-surface Atlanta to the period of the late 1800's. The restoration is complete with Victorian restaurants, saloons, boutiques, cabaret theaters, a musical museum, artist's gallery, turn-of-the-century printing shop, period signing and street furniture. The development has created added vitality and interest in downtown Atlanta, recreating much of its historic past.

New York—A Seaport Heritage

The South Street Seaport Museum is an ambitious program to preserve and restore a small element of the nautical history of New York City, in a section of the Manhattan waterfront near the historic Brooklyn Bridge. The Seaport Museum will consist of a pedestrian precinct formed by five city blocks, and a section of the waterfront containing four finger piers. Architecturally, the area restoration will save all existing buildings in the area, most of which were constructed in the period from 1820 to 1890. A major concern of the restoration project is the recreation of the streetscape of the past. This has involved much study of old paintings, prints and photos of the area. The four piers will be designed as park-like extensions of the streets. Selected ships of particular significance in New York's seafaring history will be docked at the piers and open to the public. In addition to the ships, which will be floating museums, the seaport will contain other exhibits of New York's past seaport history, including maritime, whaling, fishery, and shipping family museums. Plans for the seaport include a working shipyard, to illustrate the shipbuilding trades of the past, and a marina, to accommodate waterborne visitors. The seaport museum, which is located a short distance from the Manhattan financial district, is an important restoration not only in its historical sense, but in the sense of bringing back to New Yorkers some pride of identification with their city.

A scale model of New York's seaport museum.

Bibliography
Illustration Credits
Index

Bibliography

CHAPTER ONE – PEDESTRIAN MAN

Moore, R., "Man, Time and Fossils," N.Y., Publ. A. Knopf, 1961, pp. 57-58.

Washburn, S. L., "Tools and Human Evolution," Scientific American, Sept. 1960.

Napier, John, "The Antiquity of Human Walking," Scientific American, April 1967.

Mumford, Lewis, "The City in History," Harcourt, Brace and World Inc. 1961, 657 pp.

Benepe, B., "The Pedestrian in the City," (Traffic Quarterly, Vol. 19, No. 1 January 1965, pp. 28-42.

Rudofsky, Bernard; "Streets for People, a Primer for Americans", Doubleday & Co. Inc., 1970, 351 pp.

Dober, Richard P., "Environmental Design," Van Nostrand Reinhold Co., 1969, 277 pp.

Appleyard, D., Lintell, M., "Environmental Quality of City Streets" Center of Planning and Development Research, University of California, Berkeley, Working Paper No. 142, Dec. 1970, 44 pp.

"Manual on Pedestrian Safety" — American Automobile Association, Washington, D.C., 1964, 163 pp.

"Pedestrians" — Highway Users Foundation for Safety and Mobility (chapter 8), 1970, 9 pp.

"Pedestrian Safety" — Road Research Laboratory, Oct. 1969, 72 pp.

Sandels, S., "The Child Pedestrian" — School Safety, March-April 1970.

Yaksich, S., "Consumer Needs of Pedestrians," Proceedings, Institute of Traffic Engineers, Los Angeles, Cal., August 1969.

"Design for All Americans" — A report of the National Commission on Architectural Barriers". — U.S. Govt. Printing Office.

Noakes, E. H., "Transit for the Handicapped," Nations Cities, March 1967.

Hilleary, James, "Buildings" for All to Use — The Goal of Barrier — Free Architecture" AIA Journal March 1969.

"Transportation Needs of the Handicapped: Travel Barriers" — ABT Associates Inc. Cambridge, Mass. Aug. '69, 207 pp. and Bib. pp. 187-327.

CHAPTER TWO – HUMAN CHARACTERISTICS RELATED TO PEDESTRIAN DESIGN

Damon, A., et al, "The Human Body in Equipment Design," Harvard University Press. Cambridge, Mass., 1966, 360 p., pp. 104, 105, 134, 135.

Weisz, John D., "Human Factors Engineering Design Standards for Communications Systems and Related Equipment," United State Army Human Engineering Laboratories, Aberdeen Proving Grounds, Maryland, December, 1968 — AD 688-126.

Cohen, L. B., "Work Staggering for Traffic Relief," Praeger, New York, 1968.

Ardrey, R., "The Territorial Imperative," Atheneum, New York (1966), 162 pp.

Morris, D., "The Naked Ape," Dell (1969), pp. 140, 141, 151, 152.

Wolf, Michael, Hirsch, Verena, "The Behavior of Pedestrians on 42nd Street, New York City" —unpublished, Graduate Center, City University of

New York, 1970, 18 pp.

Hall, E. T., "The Hidden Dimension," New York, Doubleday and Company, Inc., 1966, 216 pp.

Horowitz, M. S. et al. "The Body Buffer Zone, An Exploration of Personal Space," Arch. Gen. Psychiat., 11: pp. 651-656, 1964.

Kinzel, A., "Body Buffer Zone in Violent Prisoners," Proceedings, American Phychiatric Association Meeting, Miami, Florida, May 1967.

Gibson, J. G., "The Perception of the Visual World," Houghton Mifflin Company, Boston, Riverside Press, Cambridge, 1960.

Bekker, M. G., "Theory of Land Locomotion," University of Michigan Press, Ann Arbor, 1956.

Williams, M., Lissner, H., "Biomechanics of Human Motion," Publ. W. B. Saunders Company., (1962) 1st Ed. p. 122.

Cavagna, G. A., et al. "Mechanics of Walking," Journal of Applied Physiology, 21 (1): 271-278, 1966.

Broer, M. R., "Efficiency of Human Movement," Publ. W. B. Saunders Company, (1966, 2nd Edition), pp. 107-141.

Murray, M. P. et al, "Patterns of Sagittal Rotation of the Upper Limbs in Walking," Phys. Therapy, Vol. 47, No. 4. pp. 272-284.

Murray, M. P. "Gait as a Total Pattern of Movement" Amer. Jour. Phys. Med. Vol. 46, No. 1 1967, pp. 290-333.

Smith, K. W., et al, "Analysis of the Temporal Components of Motion in Human Gait," American Journal of Physical Medicine 39: 1960, pp. 142-151.

Richardson, M., "Physiological Responses and Energy Expenditures of Women Using Stairs of Three Designs," Journal of Applied Physiology 21: May 1966, pp. 1078-1082.

Benedict, F. G., Parmenter, H. S., "Energy Metabolism of Women While Ascending and Descending Stairs," American Journal of Applied Physiology, 84: 290-291 (1929).

Callender, J. H. (edit.), Time Saver Standards — A Handbook of Architectural Design, 4th Edition, McGraw Hill, 1966, Stairs, pp. 562-571.

Lynch, Kevin — "The Image of the City" MIT Press, Cambridge, Mass. 1960, 194 pp.

CHAPTER THREE — TRAFFIC AND SPACE CHARACTER-ISTICS OF PEDESTRIANS

Drew, D. R., "Traffic Flow Theory and Control," McGraw Hill Book Company, (1968).

Murray, M. P., et al, "Comparison of Free and Fast Speed Walking Patterns of Normal Men" —Amer. Journ. Phys. Med. Vol. 45, No. 1, 1966, pp. 8-24.

MacDorman, L. C., "An Investigation of Pedestrian Travel Speeds in the Business District of Washington, D. C." Master's Thesis, Catholic University of American, May 1957.

Hoel, L. A., "Pedestrian Travel Rates in Central Business Districts," Traffic Engineering, January 1968, pp. 10-13.

"Research on Road Traffic," Road Research Laboratory, Her Majesty's Stationery Office, 1965.

Wayne, E. O., "The Effect of Treadmill Grade on Performance Decrement Using a Titration Schedule," United States Army Medical Research Laboratory, Report No. 535, Fort Knox, Kentucky, April 4, 1962.

Holmgren, G. L., Harker, G. S., "Characteristic Pace as Determined by Use of a Tracking Treadmill," United States Medical Research Laboratory, Report No. 685, November 14, 1966.

Older, S. J., "Movement of Pedestrians on Footways in Shopping Streets," Road Research Laboratory, Ministry of Transport, Traffic Engineering and Control, August 1968. pp. 160-163.

Hankin, B. D., Wright, R. A., "Passenger Flow in Subways," Operation Research Quarterly, (Great Britain) 1958 (9) (2) pp. 81-88.

Navin, P. D., Wheeler, R. J., "Pedestrian Flow Characteristics," Traffic Engineering, June 1969, pp. 30-36.

Carstens, R. L., Ring, S. L., "Pedestrian Capacities of Shelter Entrances," Traffic Engineering, Dec. 1970, pp. 38-43.

Oeding, D., "Verkehrsbelastung und Dimensionierung von Gehwegen und anderen Anlagen des Fusgangerverkehrs," Strassenbau und Strassenverkehrstechnik Heft 22, Bonn, 1963.

Baerwald, Edward J., Traffic Engineering Handbook, Institute of Traffic Engineers, Washington, D. C., 1965, pp. 108-141.

"Geometric Design of Loading Platforms and Bus Runways for Local and Suburban Bus Terminals," Traffic Engineering, January 1958, pp. 32-36.

CHAPTER FOUR — LEVEL-OF-SERVICE DESIGN STANDARDS

Highway Capacity Manual, Highway Research Board, Special Report 87, Washington, D. C. (1965).

Fruin, John J. — "Designing for Pedestrians — a Level-of-Service Concept," Dissertation, Polytechnic Institute of Brooklyn, June, 1970, 135 pp.

CHAPTER FIVE — PEDESTRIAN MOVERS "PEDMOVERS"

Annett, F., "Elevators," McGraw Hill, 3rd Edition.

Gusrae, G. — "Moving Sidewalks" Arch. Record — June 1956.

The American Safety Code for Elevators, (ASA 17.1), The American Standards Association.

"Skyscrapers Reach New Heights as Elevators Score at the Core," Engineering News Record, April 1, 1791, pp. 24-26.

Strakosch, G. R., "Vertical Transportation: Elevators and Escalators," John Wiley & Sons, Inc., New York, 1967.

Manser, A. W., "Report on Study of Escalator Capacity," London Transport, Aug. 8, 1968.

"Preliminary Information Report on Pedestrian Characteristics and Space Requirements," (unpublished) Institute of Traffic Engineers, Committee 8F.

Balfour, H. and Barrangon, M., "People Handling at the Worlds Fair," Mechanical Engineering, Aug. 1964. pp. 46-53.

Sandvik Movator, Reference List of Installations, Montparnasse Station, Paris, France.

Schriber, T. J., General Purpose Simulation System/360 Introductory Concepts and Case Studies, Preliminary Edit., University of Michigan, Ann Arbor, Mich. (Sept. 1968).

IBM Corporation, General Purpose Simulation System/360 User's Manual, H20-0326-2.

The Development and Demonstration of a Family of Practical Moving-Way Transport Systems for Pedestrians, PB 178 255, Battelle Memorial Institute, Columbis Ohio, Oct. 1967.

Caplan, Basil — "New Ways of Moving People", Mechanical Handling, Sept. 1968.

Richards, Brian — "New Movement in Cities," Reinhold Pub., N.Y. 1966, 96 pp.

"The Carveyor — Solution to City Traffic Snarls," The Goodyear Tire and Rubber Co.

"Starrcar — System Description and Application Notes," Alden Self Transit Systems Corporation.

"Dashaveyor — Revolution in Transportation," The Dashaveyor Company.

CHAPTER SIX – ELEMENTS OF PEDESTRIAN PLANNING

Stuart, D. G., "Planning for Pedestrians," Journal of American Institute of Planners, January 1968, pp. 37-41.

Morris, R. L., Zisman, S. F., "The Pedestrian, Downtown, and the Planner," Journal of the American Institute of Planners, August 1962, Vol. XXVIII, No. 3, pp. 152-158.

Welke, R. C., "Improved Pedestrian Indications Aid D. C. Drivers," Traffic Engineering, Jan. 68, pp. 26-33.

"Walking Space in City Centers," Regional Plan Association of New York — Release, May 1971.

"Staggered Work Hours Project in Lower Manhattan," Internal Report — The Port of New York Authority.

"City Malls: Fresh Life for Downtown," U.S. News and World Report, Jan. 11, 1971.

"Aerial Walkways: Big Plans for the Future," Business Week, Dec. 26, 1970.

Lessieu, E. "Pedestrian Circulation Systems," Transportation Research Forum.

"The Pedestrian Count," Amer. Soc. Planning Officials, Report No. 199, June 1965, 16 pp.

Moon, I. A., Everest, F. A., "Time Lapse Cinematography," Journal of the Society of Motion Picture and Television Engineers, Vol. 76, February 1967, pp. 81-88.

"Cameras Aloft — Project Sky Count," The Port of New York Authority Operations Services Department, Operations Standards Division, 1968.

Duitz, M., "Hours Become Seconds With Nizo Time Lapse S-80," Popular Photography, September 1968.

Street and Highway Lighting Magazine — Various Issues.

Ness, MP, et al, — "An Analysis of Central Business District Pedestrian Circulation Patterns," paper submitted to Highway Research Board, Aug. 1968.

Garbecht, D. — "Distributions of Pedestrians in a Rectangular Grid," Journ. Transport Eco. and Policy, Jan. 1970, pp. 66-88.

Brooks, Mary, "Bonus Provisions in Central City Areas," Amer. Soc. Planning Officials, 52 pp.

CHAPTER SEVEN – ELEMENTS OF PEDESTRIAN DESIGN

Stuart, D., "The Systems Approach in Urban Planning," Special Report ASPO.

Boyce, J., "What is the Systems Approach,"? Progressive Arch., Nov. 1969, pp. 118-121.

Fruin, J., — "Environmental Factors in Passenger Terminal Design," Meeting Preprint 1280 Amer. Soc. Civil Engrs. Meeting, 1970, 21 pp.

Cantilli, E., Fruin J., "Information Systems in Terminals," paper prepared for Joint ASCE-ASME Conference, Chicago 1970, 26 pp.

Meier, R. C. et al, "Simulation in Business and Economics," Prentice Hall, Inc. 1969, 369 pp.

Moore G., (edit.) "Emerging Methods in Environmental Design and Planning" — Proceedings Int. Conference Cambridge Mass., June 1968, 410 pp. MIT Press.

"Design and Application of Roadway Lighting," Pub. Street and Highway Safety Lighting Bureau N.Y.C.

Building Standards for the Handicapped, 1965 — Supplement No. 7 — The National Building Code of Canada.

CHAPTER EIGHT – NEW DEVELOPMENTS IN PLANNED PEDESTRIAN ENVIRONMENTS

"A Press Visit to the Barbican," The Corporation of London, P.O. Box 270, Guildhall, London EC2.

Pendakur, S., — "Pedestrian Circulation Systems in Canada," Highway Research Board, Jan. 1971.

"On Foot, Downtown," City of Toronto Planning Board — Dec., 1970, 12 pp. and Illus.

"Cincinnati — No Pause in Progress," City of Cincinnati — 36 pp.

"Minneapolis Skyway System," Minneapolis Planning and Development Department.

"New Street Scene," Architectural Forum, Jan.-Feb., 1969, (Nicollet Mall-Minneapolis Minn.).

"Feasibility of Moving Walks/Boston" — 5 reports 1. Overview, 2. Transportation Requirements, 3. Engineering Considerations, 4. Design, 5. Legal Considerations. — The Boston Redevelopment Authority, Boston, Mass., Jan., 1971.

"Underground Atlanta," Public Relations Department, P.O. Box 1746 Atlanta, Ga., 30301.

"South Street Seaport," South Street Seaport Museum, 16 Fulton Street N. Y., N.Y., 10038, 40 pp.

Illustration Credits

(Illustrations by author not listed)

Index